Project Team Leadership and Communication

Samuel Malachowsky, PMP

Rochester, NY, USA · www.lintwood.com

This book is dedicated to my wife, Patty, in appreciation of all of her support.

Special thanks to my editor, George Goga, for his excellent work.

Every effort has been made in the preparation of this book to find and convey accurate, truthful information. However, this book is sold without warranty, either expressed or implied. The author, publisher, distributors, or dealers will not be held liable for damages caused or alleged to have been caused directly or indirectly by this book. Use the information contained at your own risk.

Due to environmental considerations, this book may be print-on-demand. Because of this, small variations in alignment, color, and cover design may be present. Please report issues that affect overall quality or readability to the publisher.

Significant discounts are available for large orders.
Please direct inquiries to info@lintwood.com.

Instructional resources available at http://lintwood.com/ProjectLeadership

Publisher's Cataloging-in-Publication data

Names: Malachowsky, Samuel, author.
Title: Project team leadership and communication / Samuel Malachowsky.
Description: Includes bibliographical references and index. | Rochester, NY:
    Lintwood Press, 2018.
Identifiers: ISBN 978-1-7323789-1-9 (Hardcover) | 978-1-7323789-0-2 (pbk.) |
    LCCN 2018906120
Subjects: LCSH Leadership. | Project management. | Communication. | Teams in
    the workplace. | Agile software development–Management. |
    BISAC TECHNOLOGY & ENGINEERING / Project Management |
    BUSINESS & ECONOMICS / Project Management | COMPUTERS /
    Software Development & Engineering / Project Management
Classification: LCC HD69.P75 .M354 2018 | DDC 658.404–dc23

Brief Contents

Detailed Contents

About This Book

Welcome and thank you for picking up this book! It is my hope that it will return the favor by elevating your ability to lead a project team, raising your understanding of the situations you will face, and increasing your skill of effectively communicating and managing the expectations of those important to your projects.

In addition to covering the concepts implied by the book's title, a main objective of the text is to accommodate readers' varied preferences and learning styles. The writing and resources included in the text are designed to be useful to all, but your learning style will contribute to your understanding and application of the concepts and practices included.

How You Learn

I have tried to structure this book so that it appeals to the many diverse learning styles readers bring to the text.

Some readers may choose to read the book cover-to-cover in one or two sessions. To accommodate these readers, I've carefully considered which managerial concepts to include and which to omit; I've also been deliberate with the ordering of chapters and the central ideas which lead into and build on each other—these decisions will benefit the type of reader who will keep the text as a resource to reference when needed. To further support these readers, I've included an extensive table of contents, exhaustive index, and numerous cross-references throughout the text. I understand that the speed at which this type of reader can connect their need for a refresher with the material they've read is important—to these readers, value is mined out of a book on a situational basis, and they tend to have a mastery of knowing *where* to find information, thus placing less value on memorization.

Other readers prefer to intentionally limit how much they read in one sitting so they can ruminate over what they've just absorbed. Once they have completed a book, these readers are likely to never open its pages again. If they choose to keep the text itself, it's often used as a memento—these readers relish the opportunity to pass it along to another person who may find it useful, and its existence on their shelf is tied to reminding them of an experience rather than its availability to be used as a reference. To support this type of learner, I've included resources and exercises both within and at the end of chapters. These questions and scenarios are designed to deepen understanding and retention of the material, taking longer to complete but also giving the reader an opportunity to visualize and apply what they've just learned.

Finally, other readers have enrolled in a class or training that includes this book as a reference. These readers are likely to employ some combination of the two reading styles listed above. If you are one of these readers, your instructor has likely seen value in the concepts covered herein and has crafted a curriculum unique to your situation (whether academic or industry). To support this situation, the text adopts many of the conventions of a textbook, with clear chapter structure, activities, glossaries, questions and exercises, academic citation of sources, and "courseware" (slides, curricula, etc.), which are available on the publisher's website. It is my hope that you will find both the instructor's efforts and the resources you retain after training valuable, honing you as a professional and increasing your ability to cope with and manage the situations you'll encounter in the future.

Book Structure

A brief description of what each chapter covers has been included in the *Brief Contents* at the beginning of this book. Generally, chapters flow into each other and link the ideas and practical coverage of concepts into one another. To build this cohesiveness, I've liberally used cross-references throughout the text. Chapter 6, titled *Pitfalls to Identify and Avoid*, concludes the book by presenting several common (negative) scenarios, which give readers a chance to apply what they've learned appropriately to each situation if it were to occur.

In addition to content, most chapters include a "chapter tool" and additional resources after their conclusions. Each chapter tool is designed to give the reader a practical, relevant resource designed to create a measurable effect on their individual, team, or overall project development. Resources at the end of each chapter include key terms (with page references), review questions (with answers and page references on page 223), exercises (designed to deepen thought and understanding), and notes (citations, etc.).

After the conclusion of the final chapter, an appendix has been added, titled *Agile: The Future of Projects?* This chapter looks at the evolution of project management through the lens of a rapidly-expanding trend known as Agile Methods. Originally reserved for software engineering, Agile (and its most popular variant, Scrum) has been making headway in fields as diverse as mechanical engineering and agriculture. The goal of this appendix is to demonstrate Agile's relevance to *your* project by exploring its methods, values, and techniques.

Scope of this Book

"Scope," a term further discussed in chapter 2, is defined as what is and isn't included in something. The scope of this book has been intentionally limited to what new project leaders are likely to need the most. I've included concepts such as understanding how to estimate time and effort and risk management, while I've intentionally excluded managing budgets, finding personnel, and acquiring materials. (Time management is essential in all projects, and thus required in a text with this scope, but there's a good chance that a new or early-career project leader will not have wide discretionary control over their budget and human resources; in addition, they may also be required to follow standard organizational procedures for materials acquisition, thus limiting the benefits of any exhaustive discussion this text could provide.)

Another reason to limit the scope of concepts discussed in this text is brevity. The prevalence of online and bound material in each subject area should help the reader easily find the resources (beyond those in this book) that they need. Indeed, entire books are available which cover what may only warrant one page in this text. In many cases, understanding the core concepts allows readers to extrapolate and expand the concept on their own. For instance, *precedence*, a concept covered in chapter 3, includes finish-to-start task sequencing, but omits its logical counterparts, finish-to-finish and start-to-start, both because these are less common precedence types and because they are easy to understand if the root concept is clear.

In general, this book strives to provide practical and straightforward "best practices" in each area it covers. It's important to understand that this is by no means the only or even the appropriate way to approach these topics, for all readers. Organizations, industries, and teams vary quite wildly in their standards, practices, and practical approaches to many aspects of leadership, communication, and project work. With these things in mind, my hope is to raise the awareness of common practices—readers should adopt the useful elements of the text and make improvements to their team and project interactions as opportunities arise.

Dividing Your Attention

Throughout the book, I've attempted to avoid the page-after-page-of-text format found in most nonfiction. In addition to relevant illustrations, charts, graphs, and even a few cartons, you will find four types of callouts denoted by different icons:

"Think About This"
This denotes a way that you may apply a concept to your own work situation, profession, or personal life. Thinking of examples will help you remember and ultimately apply the concepts in the future.

Resource
Many of the concepts covered in this book are covered more comprehensively in other sections or chapters, and by other authors. When you see this symbol, expect to also see a cross-reference, book title, website, or other resource that will give you related or more thorough information.

Exercise
In some cases, completing a brief exercise while reading may enhance your understanding of the material. Callouts with this symbol will include instructions for completing a short exercise. Additionally, the end of each chapter includes several review questions and exercises that address the major topics discussed in that chapter.

Tool
This denotes a simple tool or concept that has the potential to assist you with planning and executing your project. Most chapters also feature or conclude with a helpful tool and related activity.

It is my sincere hope that this book has a positive impact on your future projects and your ability as a leader. Now, on to the content!

Understanding Leadership

In this introduction, we explore what it means to be a leader and how to match your leadership style, influence, and motivators with the culture of the team you are leading. Additionally, this chapter explores who is important to the project and provides a basic understanding of the field of Project Management.

Leadership means different things to each of us. To many, it means authority— the *empowerment* of telling others what to do. Alternatively, it may evoke the *responsibility*, or the *burden* of leadership. Others associate it with *honor*, *duty*, or *calling*, speaking to the *ideals* of a leader. Frequently, we debate whether leadership is a natural ability available to us from our earliest social interactions or simply a skill to be mastered with the proper training and practice. Regardless of what your feelings are about these concepts, it's important to remember that leadership is all about *people*. John C. Maxwell put it best:

> **Leadership is not about titles, positions or flowcharts. It is about one life influencing another.**[1]

John C. Maxwell
John has written many well-known books on leadership, including *The 21 Irrefutable Laws of Leadership* and *The 360° Leader*. Many consider these books required reading for effective team leadership. (They're also available in audiobook form.)

1.1   The Leader's Title

A leader can have many titles. Classics such as "Manager" and "Supervisor" refer to a specific title, but what about the experience these titles assume?

What's in a Name?
On a piece of paper, jot down the following list of terms, then quickly place 1 or 2 plus signs (+) or minus signs (−) next to each term based on how that term makes you feel: either positive (+) or negative (−).

Boss • Dictator • Teacher • Expert • Tyrant • Manager
Mediator • Coach • CEO • Parent • President • Mentor

When you read these titles, did you think of an individual in your own life? A public or historic figure? Maybe even about their leadership style?

A leader's title is most often an interpretation of *their own* leader or boss—a set of words that is supposed to represent or summarize their job function or the division, area, or field to which they are assigned. Titles rarely communicate the subtleties of what the job entails, the difficulty it contains, or the uniqueness of the team that's being led. As an example, many team leaders have *Project Manager* as their job title—the word *project* is clear enough here, but what about *manager*? Does this mean they can hire and fire people? Are they setting strategy? Or are they just managing the to-do list and a few meetings?

To find the answer, we must break down the *idea* of team leadership into its digestible components: leadership styles, types of influence, motivations, culture, and an understanding of who is being led.

1.2   Leadership Styles

Every individual has a preferred leadership style; every team does, too (part of their culture, a concept covered later in this chapter). As individuals, leaders also migrate towards a particular style. In addition to the mechanics of the leadership style itself, all leadership experiences also emphasize one of three things: the leader, the team, or the individual team members, as well as an approach that prioritizes productivity or harmony. In their book on leadership, Goleman, Boyatzis, and McKee define several key styles:[2]

Affiliative

This style emphasizes connection, harmony, and conflict resolution above all else. It's especially effective when conditions have left a team in need of "repair." Though affiliative leadership is often effective at boosting morale, it leaves a potential for abuse; poor performance can go uncorrected and team members may begin to perceive that mediocrity is acceptable as long as harmony is present. This type of leadership works best in combination with others.

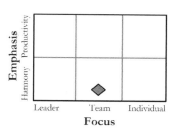

Authoritarian / Commanding / Autocratic

When many think of leadership and *authority*, this style usually comes to mind. Classically used by the military and often portrayed across media, authoritarian leadership is most effective when a team is in crisis or drastic remediation is needed. Because it relies heavily on criticism and rarely focuses on achievement, it can undercut morale and cause some of the best team members to seek options elsewhere. In most organizational structures, it's best to avoid this leadership style or to only implement it temporarily.

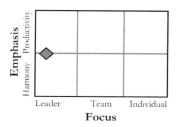

Coaching

Coaching focuses on connecting individual goals with those of the team, which shows team members how to improve their productivity. This style of leadership works best with individuals who are receptive, show initiative, and want to grow as professionals. If applied heavy-handedly, team members can feel "micromanaged," and will feel that their self-confidence is undermined. Finally, unmotivated individuals may not even respond to coaching, which requires a strategy change.

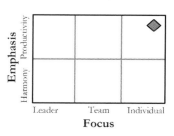

Democratic

Relying on the skills and knowledge of each team member, democratic leadership effectively fosters the group's commitment to its goals. This style works best when options or decisions are unclear and the group has mature professionals who are comfortable making decisions collectively. But, when a crisis or deadline warrants a

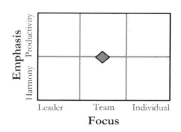

quick, decisive decision, this consensus-building technique may take too long (making another technique more appropriate).

Laissez-faire

In a laissez-faire environment, team members have complete freedom to make decisions concerning their work assignments, their pace, and how work is completed. In this situation, the leader should offer guidance or support (materials, resources, etc.) when requested or when their need is apparent. This leadership style works best when team members are extremely proficient and properly self-motivated. Though "guided freedom" is appealing to most, it requires leaders and team members to be honest about whether this style is most effective for them, and once implemented, whether it's working.

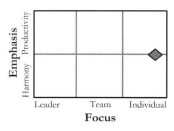

Pacesetting

A pacesetting leader has a high, almost obsessive standard for their own performance and expects team members to follow suit. Simply stated, they "lead by example." Unfortunately this type of leadership has the potential to make others feel like they're constantly failing if they can't keep up all the time. This style works best with a highly motivated team (see *Motivators* on page 7).

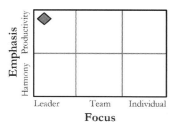

Transformational / Visionary

A transformational leader focuses on creating and communicating a vision for the future, challenging and inspiring team members with a sense of purpose and excitement. Because they're less likely to feel limited by current perceptions, these leaders are often effective when a recent failure has negatively affected the team, as they push the team to take ownership of their future success. What's more, these leaders are highly effective at addressing the mundane, stabilizing everyday situations gone awry. It's important for a transformational leader to have a realistic view of the strengths and weaknesses of each team member, which helps avoid disenchantment.

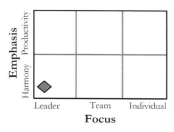

Your Preferred Leadership Style
Of those listed above, which leadership style do you prefer the leaders in your life to use? Does it differ based on the job or environment you work in? What style do you gravitate toward when leading others?

Obviously, most leaders use a *combination* of these styles, and it's important to note that their primary leadership style is often influenced by their personality, their expectations, and their own past experiences with leaders. By evaluating the needs of your team, the features of the project, and approaching the situation with a willingness to learn and adapt, you will gain the experience needed to successfully apply these leadership styles as you learn to manage teams effectively.

At the same time, it's important to remember a couple of traps you could fall into while choosing a leadership style:

- **Inflexibility:** Some leaders choose a style and never change. This can be out of habit or a fear of change and in many cases, previous success operating under that style has convinced them to keep it. However, it's important to be flexible and to choose the appropriate style when it's needed, while also having the boldness to implement it properly.

- **Circumstance:** In many cases, a leader feels that a style is preferred either because it's the best fit for their team or because they think it's superior to other styles. But in the face of deadlines, conflict, or personal difficulties, leaders may be forced to suddenly switch to a less preferred style (we've all heard of the coach who degrades into a screaming tyrant when the game isn't going well). Remember, each leadership style is useful with certain people and circumstances, but at all times, it's important to deliberately *choose* to change styles and to never let your circumstances *force* you into a less effective style.

1.3   Influence

At this point, we should distinguish between leadership *style* and how that lines up with why those you're leading choose to follow. This is called *influence*, and there are many types and combinations of influence that will help you become a stronger leader. Note that each member of a team has some influence on their peers, either positive or negative. Social psychologists John French and Bertram Raven identified five core types of influence:[3]

Formal / Legitimate

Formal influence (authority) is the classic supervisor-supervisee structure, though there may be more than one leader over each individual. Inside this multi-level hierarchical structure, power comes from individuals recognizing the authority of the leader's position. A well-known example of this is a CEO who has formal/legitimate influence over the employees, resources, and overall strategy their company must follow.

Penalty / Coercive

Penalty/coercive influence derives its power from the fear of loss or punishment. Examples of how this may play out for a team member may include the loss of one's job, a demotion, a pay decrease, or the revocation of desirable circumstances such as preferred projects or the corner office. A classic example of this is a sales manager who tells underperforming team members that they will be replaced if goals aren't met.

Reward

Reward influence often goes hand-in-hand with penalty/coercive—desirable actions are rewarded by those who hold this type of power. In addition to obvious incentives such as pay increases, those using reward-type influence can offer things like public recognition or greater autonomy (see *Motivators* in the next section). An example would be a teacher who rewards class participation with a longer recess period.

Expert

In some cases, individuals have influence because of their level of skill, experience, or knowledge, and they're labeled *experts* by those on whom they exert influence. Because there are so many areas in which someone can be an expert as well as many levels of expertise, most team members exert at least some influence on those around them. An example of expert influence might be a statistician who helps a team interpret data for a project.

Referent

Derived from trust and respect, referent influence often takes time to earn. When people are consistently happy with the way someone handles situations, their levels of trust and respect grow for that person, giving that individual influence (see *Building Trust* on page 125). An example might be a coach who is known for preventing team members from bullying one another.

Being Influenced
Of those listed above, which type of influence do you respond well to? When you think of colleagues who have had the most positive influence on you, which types of influence did they have? Which could they have used, but chose not to? Did they apply the same types of influence to everyone?

Like leadership styles, the culture of teams (discussed later in this chapter) and the personalities/past experiences of individuals mean that there are often styles of influence that are more appropriate to individual situations and team members. In some cases, using the wrong type of influence can have a detrimental effect—an example would be threatening (penalty/coercive influence) a highly qualified key team member who can easily gain employment elsewhere, where expert or referent may have been a better strategy in this situation.

1.4 Motivators

Leadership style and influence are critical components of workplace interactions, but why do we do the work we do? Living expenses are what force us to come to work, but motivators are what make us *want* to come to work. Some of the more well-known motivators include:

Money / Power
Though there are differences between them, the desire to acquire money or power is often motivating enough. These individuals are extremely interested in "moving up" or achieving the next step, expecting to earn a bump in pay or authority.

- **Classic Examples:** Salespeople, CEO's, Politicians

Recognition
Some people really want to be noticed. Although some see their professional colleagues as competition, many draw their energy from a few words of affirmation. These words, most effective if spoken publicly, validate their work and help them to feel socially accepted.

- **Classic Examples:** Entertainment, Lawyers, Interns

Interpersonal Relationships

Our coworkers have the potential to make-or-break our enjoyment in the workplace, but some people place more emphasis on a culture of cooperation. By simply spending time with a team member who is motivated by interpersonal relationships, a leader can significantly help them feel valued.

- **Classic Examples:** Religious Leaders, Social Workers

Autonomy / Interesting Work

Though few prefer the monotony of repetition, some make it their life's mission to constantly seek the new and exciting, blazing out on their own to conquer it. Though few jobs are 100% autonomous or original, these people are energized by the portion of their work that is.

- **Classic Examples:** Architects, Engineers

Purpose

Some professions have the added benefit of serving a greater purpose to society in addition to paying the mortgage. Humanitarians get a lot of attention, but that doesn't mean other professions can't derive purpose as well. People who are motivated by purpose want to feel a connection with a cause larger than themselves. Though your project may not seem to fit the bill, sometimes simply asking a team member what is important to them is enough to tap into this greater sense of purpose.

- **Classic Examples:** Doctors, Teachers, Military

Mastery / Exploration

Sometimes motivation is hard to nail down. People who are motivated by mastery or exploration are often energized by overcoming challenges and finding creative solutions to problems. Although these individuals may seem to exist in another place altogether, leaders can help hone these individuals' creative drives by providing dedicated space and resources or extending project deadlines.

- **Classic Examples:** Artists, Scientists

Intrinsic and Extrinsic Motivators
Though the reasons behind each are complex, experts generally separate motivation into two categories: extrinsic motivation and intrinsic motivation.[4] Extrinsic motivation is generally linked with an external

outcome or pressure, such as a physical reward, originating from someone else. Intrinsic motivation comes from within, and involves an inherent and internal satisfaction that comes with completing an activity.

Extrinsic Motivators	Intrinsic Motivators
Money / Power	Autonomy / Interesting Work
Recognition	Purpose
Interpersonal Relationships	Mastery / Exploration

Although certain job positions or market domains may seem to hold a correlation with one or more of these motivators, it's important that a leader doesn't assume this connection with individuals on their team. Even more important, a leader *shouldn't assume that their team is motivated by what motivates them.* As an example, the CEO of a successful startup and their team of engineers will most likely have wildly different motivators—they have different reasons for coming to work.

One of the largest dangers involved with having a diversity of motivators is that some individuals may be biased towards or against other team members' motivators. For instance, if you're primarily motivated by interpersonal relationships, you may judge someone who seeks money or power as shallow. On the other hand, if you're motivated by money, you may have a hard time believing that others are truly motivated by the interpersonal as you constantly look for their "angle." It can be hard to dissolve these types of assumptions because of a cognitive bias known as the false-consensus effect.[5] Ultimately, understanding and accepting the spectrum of motivation is important and can pave the way towards better relationships with those around us.

Even still, a bias towards one's own motivators can also be problematic. Throughout your upbringing, if those around you taught you—directly or indirectly—to value one type of motivation over another, finding yourself primarily preferring another motivator may cause internal conflict. For example, your low-paying career may give you a sense of purpose (perhaps your strongest motivator), but it doesn't help fight the feeling that you aren't really succeeding because you've internalized your parents' belief that financial security is of primary importance.

It's also important to remember that though one motivator may be more important to certain individuals, it's critical to strike the right *balance* of motivators between a team and its individuals. Obviously, few employees would show up to work with no salary even if money weren't their primary motivator, but if this primary motivator isn't regularly met, their contribution level might suffer (and they may ultimately seek other employment).

Your Motivators

After reading the text above, what are your motivators? Which is the most prominent? Are they the same as the people around you? Have they changed over time? Are they different in your personal and professional life?

A final point: there are strong, sometimes unnoticed, interactions between motivators that run the risk of becoming "demotivators." Take, for instance, a team member who scores money low on their list of motivators: If they found out that another team member, of a similar caliber, were receiving more pay, they might start feeling demotivated because they perceive this to be an interpersonal problem—which is, after all, another motivation category—between their boss and them.

Though the preceding paragraphs copiously describe the dangers of divergent motivators, it's important not to get discouraged. In childhood, we learn that trying to get others to do what we want is a part of our human reality; this realization gives us the tools we need to observe others, discern what motivates them, and try different approaches at getting what we desire. Similarly, our own motivations play a huge role in our lives (both personal and professional)—figuring out how to leverage them is an important part of the maturation process. As such, just being *aware* of the spectrum of motivation and the dangers that may present themselves is a critical first step in understanding how to appropriately motivate others—and ourselves.

The leadership styles, influences, and motivators we've discussed thus far all affect how leaders and team members work together to get things done. But what's not always clear is how these integrate into the workplaces and industries we share, creating cohesion among bosses and workers and among leaders and teams to push everyone along the path toward a final goal. The answer is *culture*.

1.5   Matching Leadership with Culture

Because leadership is fundamentally important to the success of a team and an organization, it's extremely important for a leader to understand style, influence, and motivation. Though many people rely purely on instinct when leading others, those who are more successful choose to evaluate the people, history, context, and choices available to them before using a particular leadership style. In this regard, the *culture* of an organization is extremely influential. There are many elements to culture, and anyone in a team environment must consider the following:

- The industry, domain, and nature of the business
- The history of the organization and team
- Existing leadership principles
- Organizational mission and values
- The recruitment practices of the organization or team
- Individual team members' personalities, work history, etc.
- The physical work environment or ambiance
- Stakeholders, clients, and other external parties
- The way that the team resolves disputes and communicates

These circumstances affect how an organization or team chooses to conduct business, what's valuable to them, and their global expectations inside their industry. Essentially, an organization or team's culture is its *personality.* Like people, organizations have multifaceted personalities, each influenced by the various viewpoints they assemble, adopt, and question. Often, these include:[6]

- How much risk to take in projects and in the marketplace
- Level of attention to detail
- Emphasis on outcomes or on process
- Competitiveness/aggressiveness
- Supportiveness of its members and reward structures
- Amount of teamwork vs. individual achievement
- Decisiveness and decision making methods
- Orderliness or level of bureaucracy

Leaders and experts alike spend countless hours trying to understand the culture of an industry, a specific organization, and even the acute culture of an individual friendship. An important early step in understanding culture is *awareness* of people's different circumstances and attitudes, which will help you meet them where they are with respect to their beliefs and values. Strong leaders understand the situations they will find themselves in will change; as such, they're constantly aware of various leadership styles and types of influence that help them use this constant change to their benefit. These styles become tools, helping the leader in day-to-day operations and allowing them to identify which tools are being frequently used, which may be appropriate in other circumstances, and when a strategy change is needed.

The Situational Leadership Model
Paul Hersey and Ken Blanchard's Situational Leadership Model breaks
leadership style into four basic types (telling, selling, participating, and
delegating) and matches the most appropriate type with the capability
and confidence/motivation of the individual(s) being led.[7] Telling, for
instance, involves direct, one-way communication and is best used for
inexperienced team members who are unwilling to take direct responsibility. Delegating is at the other end of the spectrum. It requires leaders
to only make important strategic decisions and to rely on team members to "get things done." For more information, search "situational
leadership theory."

1.6   Who We Lead

Though a team leader may not realize this, they are responsible for leading many
different groups. Leadership, as discussed in this chapter's introduction, doesn't
require direct authority; rather, it implies intentional interaction with others in a
way that affects the project. To really understand this, it's important to understand
the many groups with which a project leader may interact.

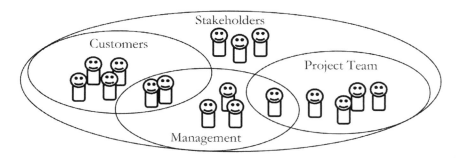

Stakeholders

Stakeholders are people who can affect or are affected by the execution or outcome
of a project. They can be identified as individuals or groups with similar characteristics and needs. It's important to always be on the lookout for new or previously
unnoticed stakeholder groups. Here's an often-overlooked example: Do members of
your team also work for other projects or departments? These other departments
or projects probably contain stakeholders who are worth your consideration.

Customers

Customers are often the most affected by the outcome of your project, though they frequently don't have visibility into its inner workings. While executing a project, it's important that the project leader advocate appropriately for this group. Note that customers may not always be external to your organization—they may be from another division, or even someone you work with on a daily basis.

Management

Management is often overlooked as a stakeholder group because, in many cases, the project leader directly reports to them or feels that they can or should advocate for themselves. What many don't realize is that this group often requires the most *intentional* leadership effort, especially considering that their ranks may overlap with other stakeholder groups.

The Project Team

The team is not only the most obvious group, but also the most vital. A team leader often needs to consider questions like: What if my team is split between another project? What about team members who are more senior or have more experience than I do? If my team members don't report directly to me in the organization, how do I lead them without formal authority?

As you've noticed, considering who is involved in a project often reveals a full circle of stakeholders: people we report to, people who report to us, people at our same level, and people outside the organization altogether are suddenly implicated in the project we've set out to complete. These combinations make the challenges, tools, and methods we must face and use circular as well. For the sake of the project and what it represents, we must *find a way* to lead those around us, even if they're our boss. This practice is part of the *discipline* of project management.

1.7   The Discipline of Project Management

Before continuing any further, it is important to address the term "Project Manager" and the discipline it entails. In its most direct form, Project Management itself can be defined as a "discipline"—a job category, which typically refers to someone who is responsible for leading a project. Somewhat related to this, but distinct in its own right, "discipline" also refers to the idea of controlling ones behavior, known as *self discipline*, which involves a range of skills and considerations.

The Project Manager

According to the Project Management Institute, a well-respected international organization known for its project management standards, local membership chapters, and professional certifications, "The project manager is the person assigned by the performing organization to lead the team that is responsible for achieving the project objectives."[8]

Because the need to manage a project is so widespread, the title this person holds can vary significantly. Many variations on this title include the word "project," such as Project Manager, Project Director, Project Planner, Project Coordinator, and Project Leader. Others invoke the word "team": Team Leader, Team Coordinator, and Team Manager. Occasionally, titles are more specific to a rank, discipline, or company's jargon, such as Implementation Manager, Delivery Manager, Program Manager, or Technical Lead. Regardless of title, these individuals are responsible for leading a team towards an established goal—this means that in order to "earn their keep," project managers must provide more value than what it costs to employ them.

Project Managers are often frustrated by knowing exactly what that word "manager" means. Those on the outside looking in may assume that it means "manager" in the classic sense—someone who has subordinates, tells them what to do, and exerts formal influence (covered earlier in this chapter) over them, including the ability to hire and fire them. Project managers know that this is often not true—in many cases, project managers don't have the ability to terminate a member of their team.

In this example, the word "manager" refers to the management of the project itself, a complex endeavor that requires a great deal of patience, endurance, and skill. If there is one feature that brings the discipline of project management together, it's the fact that the project manager must pay attention to many different aspects of a project simultaneously—time, resources, team members, results and reports, to name a few. The remaining chapters of this book break this juggling act down into digestible components and outline the core elements of every project that managers should understand in order to be successful.

Project Management Certifications

As in many other business disciplines, project managers can earn official certifications, which open doors to the job postings they seek. The Project Management Institute's (pmi.org) Project Management Professional (PMP) and Certified Associate in Project Management (CAPM) are the most well-known and respected of these certifications. Available worldwide, they require varying levels of experience, education, and the completion of a rigorous application and examination process.

Professional Discipline and Ethics

The other use of the word "discipline" refers to the domain of self control—controlling your behavior while you manage a project. Many of the concepts covered earlier in this chapter, such as choosing a leadership style, properly influencing others, and considering the culture of an organization or team are all aspects of this. Each of these requires you to consider outside factors, apply knowledge, and make decisions as best as you can in order to move forward.

But what about internal factors? What about the way we apply discipline to ourselves? Self-discipline is guided by our ethical standards, which include our personal "code of ethics." A personal code of ethics is considered by many as the basis for living in a community—the culture of that community is shaped by the individuals who are a part of it, and in turn, those people are shaped by their own ethics. This may seem simple, but as professionals we comprise many different communities: among others, these include our profession, organization, team, and the domain (or field) in which we participate. Each of these requires us to apply our own ethics appropriately.

Whether you are a team leader or a team member, you should consider the following:[9]

- **Your qualifications:** When considering taking a job or task, ask yourself if you have the skills and ability to complete the duties associated with it. Accepting work beyond your capability presents a risk to the project and your team. It's important to understand that this doesn't mean you shouldn't "stretch" yourself, but rather be honest to those around you regarding your experience and capabilities. It's also important to note that disclosing this type of information will not always result in your being pulled from the task. Sometimes it can have a positive outcome such as the project leader choosing to assign you a mentor, partner, or training program to help you gain the skills needed to complete the work.

- **Protecting information and the project:** In some cases the project you are working on might contain proprietary information; if this is the case, confidentiality is imperative. Along with this, it might at times be necessary to report unethical behavior conducted by others.

- **Directly dealing with conflict:** This means confronting conflict head-on rather than avoiding it. In most cases it is preferable to openly discuss conflict with the other party or parties rather than dealing behind their back (see *Managing Conflict* on page 126).

- **Disclosing conflicts of interest:** A conflict of interest is a situation where the concerns or motivations of two parties may be incompatible. A common example could be a supplier to a company which is owned by an employee of that company. It is important to remember that just because a potential conflict of interest exists, there isn't necessarily a problem or impropriety to be corrected—disclosure presents the opportunity to seek acceptable resolutions and move forward.

- **Maintaining an attitude of mutual cooperation:** This means considering others when making decisions related to your work. When seeking resources as a project leader, are you considering other work already in progress? As a team member, are you properly dividing your time rather than working on the tasks you prefer? Are you protecting the reputations of your team members and colleagues? When you make a mistake, are you "fessing up" to it? Are you asking others about their preferences instead of making assumptions?

- **Advocating for team members:** Whether we like it or not, individual success is often linked to the success or failure of the projects to which we are assigned. The absolute complexity of these projects can result in a skewed "view from the outside" that may have a very real—even detrimental—effect on the careers of team members. Are you taking credit for the work of others? Are team members being recognized for their hard work? Are people being unjustly blamed for failure? Is there "blamestorming" (see page 180) happening?

Most ethical decisions fall within the domains of communication and leadership and involve a series of continuous decisions made by each member of the team. By seeking to maintain a "culture of ethics," the project leader and each team member can simultaneously provide a better environment for the team and increase the likelihood of a successful project.

The Modern Project Manager
What effect does the information age have on project management? The modernization of projects and their leadership doesn't just bring computers into projects—it also brings other dynamics like shared file spaces, work-flow engines, and social-collaboration tools. Increasingly, managing a project has come to include non-tangible, virtual files, including versions of work products and documents on remote servers, online conversations that include action items/decisions/commitments to be tracked, and the very real possibility of security or information breaches. Effectively engaging as a project leader requires more than familiarity with these tools—it requires a commitment to considering their ethical implications and actively managing them on a daily (often hourly) basis.

1.8   Chapter Tool: Who We Are as Leaders

True understanding of leadership style, influence, and motivators extends beyond a basic grasp of each concept. It requires us to look at ourselves as well as those around us and observe which styles, influences, and motivators are likely to be most effective in a given situation. The "test" below is designed to help with just that.

Self-Evaluation Test
On a sheet of paper, quickly and honestly answer each of the following questions. After that, "score" your answers based on the information on page 19 and consider what the results may mean for you as a leader and a follower.

1. I believe the quality of a student's education is more influenced by:

    (a) The quality of their school
    (b) Their individual commitment to learning

2. Regarding my goals, I believe:

    (a) Reaching goals involves luck as much as anything else
    (b) I have the skills needed to reach my goals

3. When learning a new topic, I prefer to:

    (a) Become as proficient as needed in the topic
    (b) Master the topic

4. When it comes to science and art, I believe they:

   (a) Should be carried out with a specific purpose in mind
   (b) Are most effective without external motivation

5. Rank these situations from most to least frequently encountered in your professional life thus far:

   (a) Part of a team working together to solve a problem
   (b) Seeking products or solutions that effectively meet my needs
   (c) Directing others to complete work on time and at cost

6. (True/False) My coworkers and colleagues consider a person's title more important than that person's ability to reward or punish them.

7. (True/False) People generally seem to fear penalties more than they respond to the opinions of experts or rewards for their behavior.

8. (True/False) When it comes down to it, I believe people generally respond better to incentives than expert opinions or longstanding positive relationships.

9. (True/False) In the real world, an expert's thoughts on a decision will generally win out over someone who is merely respected or has the authority to decide.

10. (True/False) Most people will respond more consistently to a person who is held in respectful regard (such as an elder) than someone who has a supervisory job title or can punish them.

Answer questions 11-15 using the following scale:

1	2	3	4	5
Not At All True	Usually Untrue	Neutral	Usually True	Very True

11. I am more likely to respond to someone who has formal authority.

12. When making decisions, the fear of negative consequences is a consistent consideration I weigh.

13. Nothing motivates me more than knowing that there's a reward at the end of a task or project.

14. I hold experts in the highest regard and am more likely to take their suggestions because of their level of knowledge.

15. When someone who I have respected for a long time asks me to do something, I do it.

Self-Evaluation Test Results

Your answers to the "test" above may indicate your motivators, stakeholder experience, and preferred types of influence. Remember that the results you receive are intended to help with self-evaluation, not to dictate who you are—use this tool as a means of reflection, understanding, and consideration for who you would like to become.

Questions 1-4: Your Motivators

If you answered "a" to questions 1 through 4, you may be more extrinsically motivated.[10] If you answered "b" you may be more intrinsically motivated. For more information including which motivators lie in each category, see *Intrinsic and Extrinsic Motivators* on page 8.

Question 5: Your Stakeholder Experience

This question seeks to find your experience with each of the three major stakeholder groups. "a" indicates team member, "b" indicates customer, and "c" indicates management—this is which stakeholder group you have most commonly been a part of. This could mean that you most easily identify and understands the needs and desires of this group and that your primary experience involves dealing with one or both of the other groups. More information about each group is available on page 12.

Questions 6-10: How You Prefer to Influence Others

Our view of others is often influenced by the types of leadership we've been exposed to as well as our general outlook on life. By determining which method of influence you believe to be the most effective, these questions may provide you insight into the method of influencing others that is most natural to you. If you answered:

- True to question 6 and False to questions 9 and/or 10: Formal/Legitimate
- True to question 7 and False to questions 6 and/or 10: Penalty/Coercive

- True to question 8 and False to questions 6 and/or 7: Reward
- True to question 9 and False to questions 7 and/or 8: Expert
- True to question 10 and False to questions 8 and/or 9: Referent

More information about each type of influence is available starting on page 5.

Questions 11-15: How You Prefer to be Influenced

If we're honest about how we answered these questions, the results may vary from questions 6-10—it's not uncommon for someone to prefer to be led/influenced differently than how they naturally lead or influence others. The closer your answer is to "Very True," the more likely you are to respond to each type of influence:

- Question 11: Formal/Legitimate influence
- Question 12: Penalty/Coercive influence
- Question 13: Reward influence
- Question 14: Expert influence
- Question 15: Referent influence

More information about each type of influence is available starting on page 5.

1.9   Summary and Conclusion

By continuously thinking about how factors such as leadership style and motivators influence the way we work, leaders can create an environment that enhances the opportunity for project success. In realizing who we lead and how we influence those people, we also build the opportunity to shape the culture of a team in positive ways. Ultimately, effective project leaders are professionals who take the aspects of their work and the ethics of their behaviors seriously.

As you continue reading this book, make a mental note of what we've discussed here. Each of three primary leadership responsibilities (prioritization of work, team leadership, and communication) offer unique challenges to who we are as leaders— don't forget to consider each aspect of effective leadership while performing them!

Key Terms

Conflict of Interest: A situation where the concerns or *motivations* of two parties may be incompatible. Conflicts of interest should be disclosed (page 16).

Culture: The behaviors and beliefs that determine how an organization or team interact or work. Culture is affected by individuals on the team, the industry, or existing structure and norms (page 10).

Influence: The effect that a leader or team member has on those around them. Related to authority, there are multiple types of influence (page 5).

Motivators: The primary reasons why a team member or *stakeholder* chooses to work on or is passionate about a project, activity, or task (page 7).

Project Manager: The person assigned to lead the team that is responsible for completing the project objectives (page 13).

Stakeholder: A person who can affect or is affected by the execution or outcome of a project. A project has multiple stakeholder groups (page 12).

Review Questions

1. Which leadership style is most likely to allow individuals to choose their own tasks and priorities?

2. What properties do the affiliative and democratic leadership styles have in common?

3. You respect a coworker because of her longstanding ability as a great problem solver. What types of influence are demonstrated here?

4. A colleague seems to be more productive when working with new ideas or problems that require creativity. What is most likely to be his primary motivator?

5. Is recognition an intrinsic or extrinsic motivator?

6. The project you are leading has several people who have the potential to either help or disrupt things moving forward. What key term describes this group of people?

7. A project manager notices a distinct difference between the way her new team works verses what she's previously encountered. What concepts would you enlist in explaining why things may be different?

8. You are completing a project for the Operations Director of another divi-

sion of your organization. To which stakeholder groups does the Director belong?

9. Your company has asked you to sign a non-disclosure agreement to prevent its competitors from learning about a new product. Which ethical concern does this address?

Exercises

1. How important is a leader's title as it relates to their effectiveness? Does a title change affect the leader more than it does those being led?

2. Which type of influence do you believe is most compatible with an authoritarian style of leadership? Which is least compatible?

3. Choose three titles from those listed in the *What's in a Name?* section on page 2. For each, what do you believe is their primary leadership style, type of influence, and motivator?

4. Choose a prominent, well-known leader who has influenced you in some way. What do you believe their primary leadership style, way of influencing others, and motivators were/are?

5. Look at the list of intrinsic and extrinsic motivators on page 8 and rank them from most important to least important to you. Primarily, do you consider yourself to be extrinsically or intrinsically motivated?

6. Consider the lists of cultural elements for teams and organizations starting on page 10. What are some defining cultural characteristics of your team, organization, or field of study?

7. Your project team is designing and building an online portal for your state's Department of Motor Vehicles. Excluding your fellow project team members, list 6 stakeholders or stakeholder groups that should be involved with the project.

8. Leading a project team requires self-discipline and a careful consideration of the ethics behind every action you take. What is a scenario you've encountered where ethics were violated? What could have been done differently to ensure a more ethical outcome?

9. One important professional responsibility of project leadership is advocating for team members. Explain a situation you've encountered where a leader advocated for you or a team member? How did it make you feel?

Notes

[1] Maxwell, John C. "John C. Maxwell (Author of *The 21 Irrefutable Laws of Leadership*)". Goodreads. December 2016. https://www.goodreads.com/author/show/68.John_C_Maxwell

[2] Goleman, Daniel. *Primal Leadership: Realizing the Power of Emotional Intelligence.* Boston, Mass. Harvard Business School Press, 2002.

[3] French, J. and Raven, B. *The Bases of Social Power.* In Studies in Social Power, D. Cartwright, Ed., p. 150-167. Ann Arbor, MI: Institute for Social Research. 1959.

[4] Ryan, Richard M. and Deci, Edward L. *Intrinsic and Extrinsic Motivations: Classic Definitions and New Directions.* Contemporary Educational Psychology. 25 (1): 54–67. 2000.

[5] Myers, David. *Exploring Social Psychology (7th ed.).* McGraw-Hill Education. p. 38. 2015.

[6] O'Reilly, C. A., III, Chatman, J. A., and Caldwell, D. F. *People and organizational culture: A profile comparison approach to assessing person-organization fit.* Academy of Management Journal, September 1991. p. 502, 516. 1991.

[7] Hersey, P. and Blanchard, K. H. *Management of Organizational Behavior 3rd Edition - Utilizing Human Resources.* New Jersey/Prentice Hall. 1977.

[8] Project Management Institute. *A Guide to the Project Management Body of Knowledge – Fifth Edition.* Project Management Institute Inc. p. 16. 2013.

[9] Though the considerations listed here are common to many codes of ethics, this list includes elements from the Project Management Institute's 2006 *Code of Ethics and Professional Conduct.*

[10] These questions are based on the work of Ryan, Richard and Deci, Edward L. *Intrinsic and Extrinsic Motivations: Classic Definitions and New Directions.* Contemporary Educational Psychology. 25 (1): 54–67. 2000.

Project Fundamentals

This chapter lays the foundation for understanding the nature of projects. In addition to establishing what a project is and the terminology used by project teams, it also explores the organizational structures projects live in and the early steps required to begin a project.

Having already looked at yourself as a leader and a follower, it's natural to turn your attention to the work at hand: the project. Understanding the project goes beyond comprehending its expected result—it involves distinguishing it from other types of work, understanding the environment it operates in, seeing the bigger picture, and exploring its objectives and goals at multiple levels. Because projects are complex, additional effort is needed to understand the appropriate order of execution as well as how to approach hard-to define concepts like *quality*. Finally, the practical measures of starting a project such as writing a project plan and holding a kickoff meeting must be addressed.

2.1 What is a Project?

In order to properly understand what a project entails, we must first explore where it comes from. In most cases, a project arises from a problem that needs to be solved or an opportunity that has the potential to be exploited. After identifying the problem or opportunity, sometimes called a *business need*, the *project sponsor(s)* explores the desirability of different options to determine whether the potential impact of the project is worth the investment in time and resources. Once a decision has been made to move forward, a *project charter* is created.

The Project Charter and the Project Sponsor

Does the project leader initiate the project, or does a project itself generate the need for a project leader? The answer to this chicken-and-egg problem lies in the *project charter*. This document describes the need that the project is designed to address, specifies where project funding will come from, and identifies parties important to the project (stakeholders). These three things come together to define, fund, and authorize the project leader to begin working on the project. The *project sponsor* is the individual (or group) who has the authority to write or approve the *project charter*, and is typically a prominent stakeholder.

Project Manager vs. Project Sponsor

Who is ultimately responsible for the success of the project, the project manager or the project sponsor? The project sponsor is primarily responsible for the origination, financial support, and championing of the project to parties outside the project's "circle of control." The project manager's responsibilities lie primarily within the boundaries of the project itself and are constrained by the cost, scope, and schedule available (covered later in this chapter, starting on page 43).

Defining "Project"

It would be impractical to move any further without a proper definition of what a "project" is. According to the Project Management Institute's *Project Management Body of Knowledge (PMBOK)*, a project has two defining features:[1]

- A defined beginning and end (i.e. it's temporary), and
- Unique goals and outcomes

Some have observed a third feature common to many projects:

- The need for team members with varied skills

Projects differ from *operational work*, which is often considered "business as usual." (Operational work is generally not unique. It's often repetitive, and continues until it's no longer needed, rather than seeking a defined endpoint.) Though varied skills are sometimes required for operational work, the application of these skills is usually less dynamic than in a project environment. Because project outcomes are unique by definition, it may be more difficult to predict beforehand precisely which skills are needed. While projects and operational work do share many core competencies, the management techniques needed for each are quite different.

Is it a Project?
In some cases the distinction between projects and operational work can be rather difficult to define. One example is maintenance, including applying security patches to a server or changing parts on a machine. Though individual efforts may be unique during certain defined periods, the "larger picture" is somewhat repetitive and ongoing. Most professionals would define these as projects (because they are more dynamic than typical operational work) but understand that they require slightly different skillsets and strategies than the type of project work focused upon by this book.

Project Phases

Typically, projects include the following general phases, known collectively as the *project life cycle*:[2]

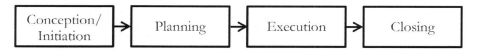

- **Conception/Initiation Phase:** During initiation, research is conducted and decisions are made regarding the feasibility of the project itself. Once the decision has been made to move forward, a project leader/manager is chosen, rough planning is completed, and the team begins to take shape. Project goals, scope, and requirements (discussed in section 2.5 of this chapter) are formulated and agreed upon by stakeholders. Additionally, the essential structures and rules needed to successfully complete future phases are put in place.

- **Planning Phase** In this phase, plans are drafted in more detail. Although these plans include obvious elements such as the schedule (see *Project Scheduling* on page 88) budget, and product designs, they should also include elements such as the communication plan (discussed in chapter 5), how quality should be tracked (discussed later in this chapter in section 2.4), and how the final product is to be delivered to the customer.

- **Execution Phase** This is where "the rubber meets the road" and the bulk of the project work is completed. More specifically, the plans created in the previous phases are implemented. Because progress is being made, it is essential that other important activities such as schedule tracking (see *Project Tracking* on page 94) and communication take place on a regular basis. Complex or multi-phase projects may move between the planning and execution phases multiple times.

- **Closing Phase** The final phase ensures that previous efforts are appropriately brought to an end. This involves hand-off to the customer and the release of professional responsibility. It also requires equipment, personnel, and budgets to be properly accounted for. During this phase, one essential duty that's often neglected is the collecting and properly disseminating of *lessons learned* so that future projects can benefit from the successes and failures experienced during the project (see *Lessons Learned* on page 170).

In addition to the four sequential project life cycle phases, one additional element must be considered:

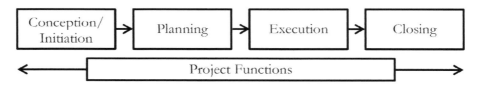

- **Project Functions** This element of the project life cycle is differentiated from the others because its activities don't generally occur at a specific time. Instead, they are (ideally) implemented and monitored continuously. Examples of project functions include:
  - Risk Management (covered in chapter 3 on page 97)
  - Quality Assurance (covered later in this chapter on page 43)
  - Communications Management (covered in chapter 5)
  - *Project Management* itself meets the definition of a project function (a major theme of this book)

The nature of each of these competencies requires an element of monitoring: making decisions based on what is observed and taking action based on those decisions. For example, a project leader must continuously monitor the morale and effectiveness of their team, make choices about how to proceed, and enact those decisions within the project. If the task "check morale of team" were planned ahead of time at one singular point in the timeline, its benefit would be minimal. To be effective, this type of action must be continuous.

It's important to understand that the phases and elements within a project often exist as part of a larger ecosystem. Many projects are single components in a much larger effort which themselves could also be considered a project (i.e. the bigger effort, sometimes called a *program*, is also unique and has a defined period). This can play out so that the steps you might expect a project to include each become their own "sub-project":

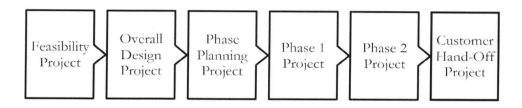

At first glance, it may seem like a project centered around creating a design makes little or no sense, but the "product" (the design document) is unique and requires planning and implementation just like any other project. If we relate the example to the project of building a retail center, the idea seems more commonplace because the scale and complexity of each step becomes obvious:

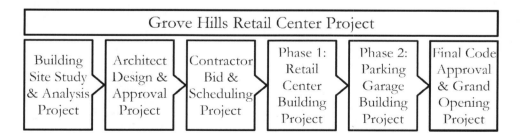

In addition to projects that encompass a small part of a single effort, some projects are part of a product's *life cycle*. Each stage of a product's life could include one or more projects:

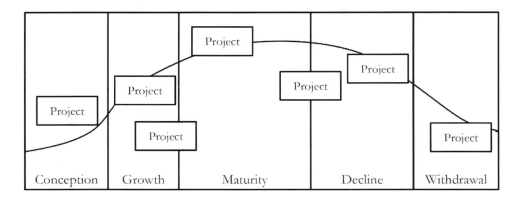

For example, a factory producing and selling a particular good (production and sales themselves are often *operational work*) could have the following projects:

- Introductory marketing
- Initial setup of production machinery
- Introduction into new markets or retail chains
- Realizing savings and efficiencies from mass-production ("economies of scale")
- Increasing production capacity
- Final closure of the production line
- Converting the machines for another use or selling them to another company

Each of these projects would contain the four life cycle phases or could themselves contain sub-projects.

Now that we've gained some insight into what a project *is*, let's move on to the environment in which it *lives*.

2.2   The Project Environment

There are many factors beyond the goals of a project that affect its nature. The size or structure of a project, discussed in the previous section, is one example of this. Another element that has a huge effect on projects is the culture of the organization (discussed on page 10 in chapter 1). The very structure of the organization itself also affects its projects. By examining different structures, we can begin to draw conclusions about that effect, particularly as it pertains to resources and personnel. Experts generally divide organizations into three main types: functional, project-focused, and matrix.[3]

Functional Organizations

In many ways, the functional organizational structure is the "classic" structure and is typically divided by specialty, with multiple layers of hierarchy in each functional area. In most cases, this structure of "silos" sees little cross-functional cooperation—divisions such as marketing, IT, human resources, and operations only share managers at the highest executive levels.

Structuring an organization in this manner may increase its efficiency. This is because resources with similar skill-sets are in close proximity, which in turn allows more efficient management, hiring practices, and cross-training. Though quite efficient for operational work, projects are forced to draw resources from multiple departments, and the project leaders themselves often report to one of them.

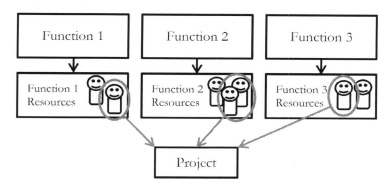

Because of the need to draw resources from multiple functional areas, this structure has the potential to present multiple difficulties during the project:

- **Authority:** Though the project leader is responsible for the success of the project, they rarely have direct, formal authority over all members of their team. If difficulties arise, the best course of action is often to seek support from a resource's functional manager, but this can be slow and inefficient and can be especially problematic if that manager tends to agree with their subordinate. This type of "bureaucracy" can be extremely damaging to projects with tight schedules or vital outcomes.

- **Priority:** The stark reality is that projects rarely get "100%" of any functional resource's time assigned to them—it's not uncommon for a functional manager to "lend" 25%, for example, of a resource's time to a project effort. These resources almost always continue to have responsibilities (typically operational work) in their home department, and they themselves frequently need to make decisions about prioritizing project and departmental tasks.

Because projects are, by their very nature, temporary, it's easy for the permanence of operational work to dominate the workplace—resources are, after all, hired and evaluated by their operational manager whose primary focus is on operational work. This situation becomes even more complicated when resources are further divided, at say 50% operational work, 25% "project A," and 25% "project B"—now even more priorities must compete for a single resource's time.

- **Vision:** In many cases, only the project sponsor and project leader have a proper view of the "big picture," which includes both the problem or opportunity the project is designed to address and the plans, tasks, and outcomes the project hopes to realize. Projects are complicated; they are often designed to benefit multiple functional areas of an organization, and they often "borrow" resources unevenly. Because of this, certain parts of the project may seem more important or beneficial to certain functional managers while other parts do not.

Though there are obvious difficulties involved, it's important not to get discouraged. Functional organizations regularly complete successful projects and their managers often have a great deal of experience in lending support to ongoing projects. From the project's perspective, these managers are key stakeholders who need to be properly accounted for while planning and execution are underway (see *Who We Lead* on page 12). Finally, a core advantage of a functional organization is the depth of resources available to a project; if a team member leaves or becomes unavailable, there's a good chance that there's a viable replacement in their home department.

Who Does the Project Manager Report To?

In a purely functional organization where all resources fall under functional "silos," who does the project manager work for? The answer can vary, but two scenarios are common. In many cases, especially if projects are smaller, one of the functional areas provides the project manager. (This is usually the "silo" that has the most interest in the project.) In other cases, the project managers have their own functional area, known as the *Project Management Office*, or PMO.[4] This office typically defines organization-wide project standards, hires project managers, assigns them as needed, and coordinates projects that require interaction to succeed. This can benefit projects that affect multiple departments, since favoritism (or its appearance) is less likely to occur.

Project-Focused Organizations

At the other end of the spectrum are project-focused organizations. They have min-imized functional structure and are often rather "flat," meaning there are very few layers of management between the bottom and top. Project-focused organizations are defined by resources' primary attachment to individual projects rather than a department or division. Because of this, project leaders tend to have much more direct authority over team members—they are often directly involved in searching for, hiring, promoting, and terminating the employment of resources.

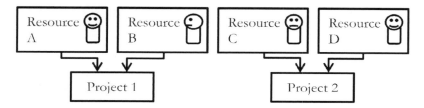

Because this structure is radically different from a functional structure, the issues affecting projects in functional organizations (authority, priority, and vision) are minimized. Instead, the project is more likely to experience issues similar to those of a stand-alone organization:

- **Competition:** Though competition is often seen as a good thing, competi-tion between projects within the same organization can have negative effects, especially when it comes to finding and retaining resources and team members. The temporary nature of projects means that team members must seek new projects as old ones come to an end, often in order to remain employed. This can result in the temptation to "jump ship" as soon as a longer-running or more desirable project becomes available. Vital projects that are nearing an end or are otherwise less desirable can be left starving for resources, struggling to complete their objectives and meet their schedules.

- **Viability:** Because each project is essentially independent, greater demands are often present regarding its "return on investment." Whether designed to meet a stated need, address a problem, or turn a financial profit, projects in this environment must consistently demonstrate the potential for a net-positive outcome. Because of this, projects that exceed resource or time constraints face cancellation—even projects that are "on track" are regularly compared to other projects to decide if they remain a solid investment. This reality often requires the project leader or sponsor to continuously advocate for the project within the larger organization, which can take time away from managing the project itself.

- **Autonomy:** One advantage of functional organizations includes the functions served by resources' "home department"—things like recruitment efforts, coverage of absent resources, training, and establishing a career path for employees. The absence of these elements means that individual projects shoulder the load for each resource and have difficulty gaining the efficiencies enjoyed by larger departments. The independent nature of the project teams can also make it difficult to appreciate the *lessons learned* (see page 170) from previous projects: a disincentive to share these and benefit "competing" projects may even appear.

Once again, it's important not to become discouraged. Projects and their teams can benefit greatly from this structure, as they are essentially the most important part of the organization—the freedom afforded to them (and in some cases the competitive nature) can strongly motivate project leaders and their team members. As a result, decisions are made faster, stakeholder lists are shorter, and the "dead weight" of underperforming team members is often lessened. In industries with a highly-mobile workforce, the perpetually temporary nature of this structure can also hold appeal. Some of the most modern and profitable organizations attribute a good portion of their success to the project-focused model.

Matrix Organizations

By their very nature, functional and project-focused organizations represent the extremes of organizational structure; sometimes they are even too extreme to be realistic. Usually, a combination of the two is either planned or happens naturally as the organization grows and adapts to new challenges. The projects carried out by *matrix organizations* often include both functional and project-focused resources.

Weighing the benefits and drawbacks of matrix organizations involves determining whether they are more functional or project-focused, or whether they are balanced between the two. Organizations with a more functional matrix, sometimes called a "weak matrix," are more likely to experience difficulties of authority, priority, and vision (detailed previously). Likewise, organizations leaning towards a project matrix (or "strong matrix") may struggle with problems related to competition, viability, and autonomy. Balanced matrix organizations may deal with all or few of these problems, depending on how that balance is achieved. It's important to note, however, that all matrix organizations seek to mitigate the issues of either extreme by importing benefits from its opposite.

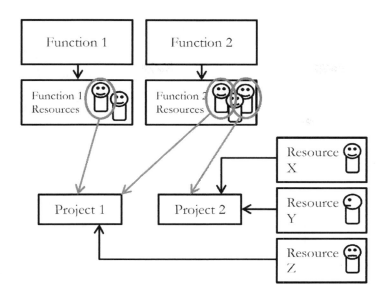

Matrix organizations can experience stresses and power struggles when deciding how to populate project teams. Functional and project managers will often prefer a structure that gives their "side" more power or influence—the project, of course, can suffer as a result. As the project progresses, these struggles are often expressed as cuts in funding, personnel, resources, or deadlines. Matrix organizations can also choose to bring in outside resources, outsource parts of the project, and hire contractors; because of their temporary, detached nature, these parties may not be as committed to the success of the project (this is an example of *Ineffectively Adding Resources to the Team*, covered on page 186).

Well-balanced matrix organizations regularly reap benefits from both functional and project-focused models: less redundancy, generally more balanced teams, and less competitiveness between projects. Because of their mixed nature, the number of stakeholders is typically increased, which generally creates more work for the project leader, but also allows the project to draw ideas and support from a bigger group. Projects within matrix organizations tend to be more outcome-oriented.[5]

Functional, project-focused, and matrix organizations are defined by both the practicalities of their existing structure and the culture of their personnel and teams. The nature of the projects they must complete also affects which type of structure an organization prefers.

2.3   Values, Needs, and Process

Just as organizations vary in how they organize projects and the resources assigned to them, there are many different ways an organization can choose to execute their projects. Understanding the organization and project's values and needs is necessary when planning how a project is to progress.

A project and organization's values can vary quite dramatically in several different categories. The word "value" speaks to what's most important to an organization, team, or project. Examples of values include:

- **Prominence of the customer's input:** Are we relying more on the customer or our team to decide what is produced?
- **Risk aversion:** How developed is the organization's ability to deal with uncertainty (for more on this, see *Risk Management* on page 97)?
- **Schedule predictability:** How important is it to know exactly when things are to occur?
- **Preferred experience level of staff and managers:** Do they typically employ lower-cost/entry-level or more expensive/experienced professionals?
- **Perception and visibility to the customer:** Is the customer's view of the project's progress extremely important?

In addition to the values that establish the themes of how work is done, there are also needs that vary from project-to-project. Understanding these variations is essential when plotting the course forward. Examples of these needs include:

- Resources and time required for the project's size and complexity
- The level of documentation needed as the project progresses and the level needed at delivery
- A need to clarify requirements, specifications, and external variables as the project continues
- Flexibility in reacting to change as the project progresses
- The need for prototypes and the ability to evolve designs before completing the final product
- Whether the project calls for a defined end-point or an ongoing effort

Why are these important to your project? An organization's values and a project's needs are heavily considered when choosing whether or not a potential project should be carried out at all. An extreme mismatch between the two may indicate that the project isn't a good idea, is likely to fail, or should even be outsourced. When choosing the project leader and team members, a solid understanding of these values and needs is also important. Those assembling the team should consider whether the skills, experiences, and personalities of potential resources are a strong match.

Once the decision is made to move forward, values and needs affect the way in which project phases and steps are carried out—this is known as the project's *process model.*

Whether they are aware of it or not (and whether they're documented or not), most organizations have processes that they follow when completing work. For project work, process models generally fall into one of three categories: *plan-focused, cyclical,* or *change-focused.*[6] In some cases, the project team is allowed to decide which is appropriate; in others, a formal decision has already been made by the organization or is dictated by the standards of the industry.

Plan-Focused Process Models

Plan-focused process models place the highest value on planning ahead and considering what will happen before moving forward with the project. In general, plan-focused models require focus on one phase or step at a time, taking the time to ensure that plans have been laid out for the future before proceeding. At the most basic level, this model resembles a waterfall.

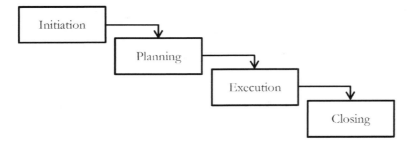

Note that this is merely an abstraction—what happens in each block as well as the number of blocks can vary from project to project.

There are several advantages inherent to this type of process. Because each phase is distinct, team members can have very specific skills and, as a result, be secured as needed. A building project, for example, doesn't need to plan wall finishes or hire drywallers as ground is being broken, but the project leader knows when those decisions and actions will need to be made. This process can be very efficient when requirements or specifications are well understood. It is also the easiest process model to understand, which allows less experienced team members to navigate it effectively.

If needed, it can also be modified to accommodate "sub-projects" with smaller teams.

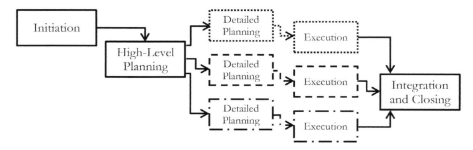

Though appropriate for many projects, there are some significant disadvantages that can present themselves in certain circumstances. Unless the customer or manager is working daily with the team, it can be hard to know just how far along the project has come (the project's *visibility*). Often the end of phases (represented as blocks in the diagram) is the only time when anyone knows for certain. Additionally, this process model handles changes in requirements or specifications poorly, often requiring a major re-planning and re-work effort—it assumes (or hopes) that all of these types of decisions are made early and won't change down the line.

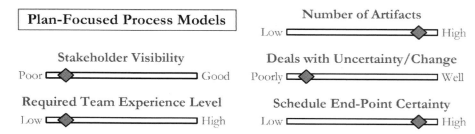

Cyclical Process Models

In some cases a project team is committed to following a plan, but knows that the project will build on itself or need to evolve before final delivery. Early project steps are often similar to plan-focused processes, but at some point these projects necessitate some sort of repeating cycle.

One way that this can manifest itself is an *incremental* approach. Once the initial high-level analysis and planning is completed, the project cycles through several steps, delivering an ever-expanding result each time.

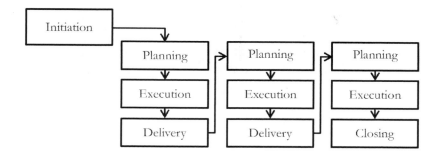

Incremental processes are commonly used for projects that are logically segmented, such as a multi-building shopping plaza or a web-based software project. In some cases, the project is limited by the funds and resources available—there simply isn't enough money or personnel to complete the whole project at once.

If a project doesn't require delivery more than once but there's still a need to verify that things are on the right track, an *iterative* process may be more appropriate.

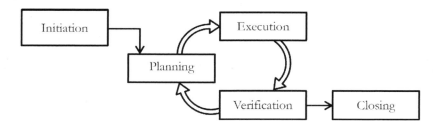

Iterative processes verify each cycle before proceeding to the next, incorporating feedback into future cycles. The most readily understandable example of this is prototyping. Here, the team creates and then improves on something, verifying with stakeholders that they are moving in the right direction before proceeding. As an example, an architect may show their rough design to the customer before moving forward with finer details.

Because delivery or verification happens so often, customer and management visibility is usually good for cyclical projects. Inexperienced teams may have trouble with the discipline required to follow the same steps over-and-over again, so strong leadership is often required to commit to this type of process.

All cyclical processes share a rather important weakness: it can be difficult at times to know when you are done. There can be a perpetual temptation to complete one more increment or iteration—both the team and the customer are enticed by this, often saying "we could make it just a bit better" (see *Scope Creep* on page 187). Combating this requires a solid definition early on regarding what the project is trying to accomplish, along with the discipline to stop when that definition has been met (defining project outcomes properly is covered later in this chapter on page 51).

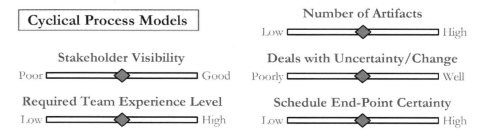

Change-Focused Process Models

In some cases, project work requires a great deal of change because it is based on shifting markets or stakeholders who are uncertain about what is needed to solve their problems. When this happens, project teams may feel that they are trying to hit a moving target and become afraid that the solution they create may miss it entirely. Change-focused process models rely heavily on important stakeholders (such as the customer) to operate as decision makers at each step of the process.

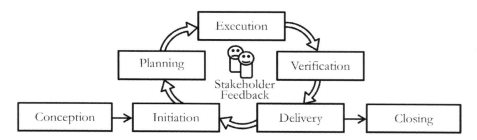

In this model, management and customer visibility are usually very high—stakeholders are regularly consulted by the team and participate in each step as it occurs. This has the potential to backfire, however, if stakeholders are unwilling or unable to participate in the process, as the sudden absence of even one significant stakeholder can have a devastating effect on the project. Risks like this can be managed (see *Risk*

Management on page 97), but if it seems that stakeholders won't be consistently available throughout the project life cycle, choosing another process model may be necessary.

This type of project requires an experienced team—each member must be able to effectively communicate, plan, execute, and verify their work on a regular basis. Whereas other models allow for a single point of contact between the stakeholders and the team, the need for continuous stakeholder feedback makes this impossible with change-focused process models. Team members must be able to understand what the team members are saying, and sometimes more importantly, they need to be careful not to commit to results that are beyond the intent of the project or capabilities of the team. This type of balancing act requires highly trained, competent, multidisciplinary team members. Because their individual members must be so strong and because stakeholders must be constantly involved in the project, teams employing a change-focused model may not have a formal leader, instead choosing to rotate or share leadership responsibilities as a unit.

Change-focused processes clearly share one main feature with cyclical processes, a repeating incremental/iterative delivery model. Because of this, they come with the same danger of never reaching completion, adapting and growing in perpetuity and taking on the characteristics of operational (ongoing, not time-limited) work. Once again, strong team members are key—they must know when to end the project, celebrate its completion, and move on to a new challenge.

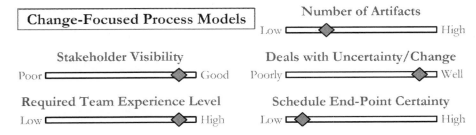

Agile Methods

The most well-known change-focused process models are known as *Agile Methods* and were developed by the software engineering community in response to the increased pace of business and consumer demand in the late 1990s and early 2000s. The appendix to this book, entitled *Agile: The Future of Projects?* (page 195) covers these concepts in more detail and offers some practical advice for applying them to your project.

Abstract to Exact

Mature organizations and teams have a clear view of their needs and values, and understand that the very way they work, their processes, are directly related to those values and needs. Though processes can be generalized into the three types covered above, they are merely an *abstraction* or model of how the work is carried out. The "blocks" in the processes can vary, and the classification refers to the general shape or flow of the steps. It's up to the organization or team to define exactly how these things should be carried out in a way that makes sense within the context of their values and needs. As an example, a company's "Gather Requirements" process may have extremely detailed steps:

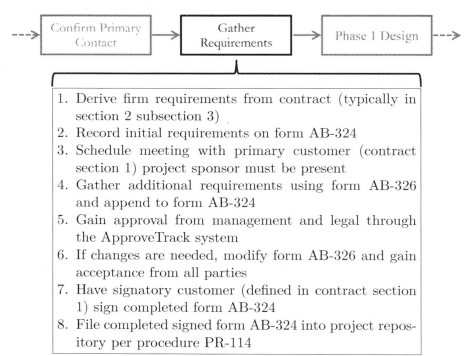

1. Derive firm requirements from contract (typically in section 2 subsection 3)
2. Record initial requirements on form AB-324
3. Schedule meeting with primary customer (contract section 1) project sponsor must be present
4. Gather additional requirements using form AB-326 and append to form AB-324
5. Gain approval from management and legal through the ApproveTrack system
6. If changes are needed, modify form AB-326 and gain acceptance from all parties
7. Have signatory customer (defined in contract section 1) sign completed form AB-324
8. File completed signed form AB-324 into project repository per procedure PR-114

Note that this process references external forms and processes which are standard to the organization. By using these existing "process assets," the project team is able to capitalize on previous improvements to the processes and record their project information in a way that is readily understood by other parties and future projects—one benefit of standardization.

The way that organizations or teams choose to document their processes can vary. In some cases, the establishment of departments or functional areas of the organization will include efforts to define key processes. In others, the team leaders or members are responsible for this documentation. In either case, it is generally necessary to record these processes—so they can be repeated, improved, shared, and used in training new team members.

ISO 9001 Certification

One common way that organizations define their processes is in compliance with ISO (International Organization for Standardization) 9001 certification.[7] Gaining this certification requires organizations to document the processes that they intend to use, follow them, and be able to prove that they have done so (through documentation in an audit after the fact). The ISO, organizations seeking 9001 certification, and customers requiring their suppliers to have certification believe that the audit process coupled with self-reflection beforehand will actively promote process improvement and a customer-focused quality approach.

2.4 Quality and The Project Triangle

Every project, product, and service out there has some concern when it comes to quality. Though it is clearly important, the term "quality" is notoriously hard to define concisely; words like "excellence," "superiority," and "distinguish" are often used when trying to define what it means. Some of these difficulties relate to perception—each individual's, or in our case, stakeholder's, perception of what quality means can have a palpable effect on every element of the project. Often, as team leaders or professionals, we find our views on quality are considerably different from customers' or users'.

One large set of distinctions in quality relate to the type of outcome the project is designed to deliver. A physical product's quality is often determined by physical attributes measured against the expectations of the customer. David Garvin, a well-known expert in quality, lists elements such as performance, features, durability, and aesthetics as important attributes.[8] When the project is producing something nonphysical, (typically a service), quality often focuses primarily on customer satisfaction; these views and opinions become the most important measure of success. When the project is creating something somewhere in the middle such as software, documentation, or an advertising product, thoughts about quality also reside in that middle space—customer satisfaction is measured in addition to the attributes of the project outcome itself.

So, given the wide variability in how quality is defined, how do we narrow things down? For most project-focused teams, there are three main quality concerns:

1. **Standards:** Engineers follow the engineering process. Scientists follow the scientific method. Accountants audit their work. People who work with hazardous materials follow standard safety procedures. Web designers place the "login" button at the top right of the site. By considering and following established standards, regulations, procedures, and best practices, a project team is able to gain the benefits and meet the expectations that prompted the creation of those standards in the first place.

2. **Conformance:** Another name for this can be "explicit quality";[9] it relates directly to the requirements, specifications, designs, or other outcome definitions created for the project. (These are covered more thoroughly in the next section, starting on page 51.) These documents represent a commitment by the project team to the stakeholders. Determining whether the project is meeting these commitments defines quality at the most basic level. Later in the process, commitments regarding schedule and budget will also be seen as elements of the project that the team should conform to as strictly as possible. Working to meet these aspects is the most straightforward way that a team can seek to achieve quality, and it's often the most directly measurable way as well.

3. **Excellence:** Considering excellence in the pursuit of quality goes beyond simply meeting the basic objectives and standards described above—it involves thinking about the project from multiple perspectives. Does the project really solve the problem for the customer? When work is in progress, am I thinking about the people who will be working after me? Are the outcomes worth the time and resources expended in getting there? Could we improve this somehow? What about the project's long-term viability—did we consider aspects like its maintainability, adaptability, or durability? These questions speak to the *implicit* quality and added value of the project's expected outcomes. Excellence can be hard to measure, but it's an important factor nonetheless.

These three concepts relate primarily to the outcome that the project is trying to bring about, but, as discussed in the beginning of this section, a fourth concept must be considered as well.

4. **Perception:** Perception of quality usually refers to the view of the stakeholders for whom the project is completed. When considering this, it's important to understand that this pertains primarily to the project as it is *in progress*—this is in contrast with the concepts listed above, which are mostly focused on the project's end result. As a team leader, managing this aspect of quality requires:

- attention to interactions (professionalism, frequency, etc.) between the team and the stakeholders,
- consideration of internal and external visibility into process and project elements, and
- careful planning of content and frequency of communication, an element of *expectation management* (covered in chapter 5 on page 171).

Considerations of these elements extend beyond the team leader, as team members should also monitor the perceptions of stakeholders and report their status to those responsible for managing them. Every member of the project team should also consider how their own actions and communications may be perceived by third parties.

Quality for *Your* Project

Thinking about quality from the perspective of your industry, organization, or team can be at overwhelming, especially since many of the concepts involved are so abstract. Starting on page 69, this chapter's practical tool (*Chapter Tool: Planning Project Quality*) is designed to help you focus on which quality attributes are most important to you, your team, and your project.

As you have probably already gathered, project quality is in many ways a discipline of achieving balance. The efforts, resources, and time expended in the pursuit of standards, conformance, and excellence (as well as perception) must be weighed against the value of the project's outcome. Put another way, the project's *cost of quality* must be properly balanced against its *cost of poor quality*.[10] Examples of each are illustrated on the next page:

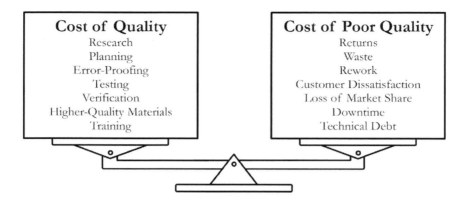

Cost of Quality	Cost of Poor Quality
Research	Returns
Planning	Waste
Error-Proofing	Rework
Testing	Customer Dissatisfaction
Verification	Loss of Market Share
Higher-Quality Materials	Downtime
Training	Technical Debt

Technical Debt

What is technical debt? Also known as design debt, it involves taking an easier solution now fully knowing that it will cost the organization more later on in the project.[11] By rushing decisions, skipping important elements such as proper documentation, and ignoring standards, projects can appear to be further ahead than they actually are. When this (often hidden) debt is finally paid, it almost always requires more effort than if it had been completed correctly in the first place.

Though a simple idea, the actual effort of balancing a project's cost of quality and cost of poor quality is quite difficult, mainly because of the word *cost*. If you asked most people what cost means, you are likely to hear something relating to money— maybe something transactional like "bang for your buck," which implies trading currency for something. But the word "cost," however, means much more than that. It can mean time expended, such as the hours spent at work rather than with friends or family. It can mean a balancing act, as in the extreme cost of being perfect vs. that of being good enough, which forces us to consider terms like "timeliness" or "value." The complexity of these ideas is most readily illustrated with *the project triangle*:

The idea of the project triangle is simple: there is a continuous relationship between scope (what is and isn't included in a project), resources (which are expended as the project continues), and schedule (the time needed). The "triple-constraint" balance between the three means that it is impossible to make changes to one without affecting at least one of the others in some way—this is why some call this "the iron triangle." Put another way, the project triangle illustrates the trade-offs that are a constant reality when completing a project.

Many of us make similar trade-offs as part of our daily lives. Public transportation, for instance, usually costs less but takes more time than taking a taxi or driving your own car. Purchasing goods at a convenience store is quicker and available at later hours, but is almost always more expensive than shopping at a grocery store. A faster, cheaper, drive-through car wash isn't as thorough or customizable as having your car detailed by hand, but is the budget-friendly norm. Like these examples, the extent of what can be done during a project, the time it takes, and the resources expended can (at varying levels of efficiency) be traded for each other; this, in turn allows for some degree of flexibility in a project. At the inception of a project, one of the three sides is often already established as the most important (the shortest possible schedule, for example) and, in following, stakeholders may have already established expectations in line with this.

Resources

Other commonly used terms for this concept are *capital* or *budget* (or *cost*, but references to *cost* earlier in this section could include a schedule or scope cost, i.e. the *cost* of quality). These represent the simple fact that money is the universal medium when it comes to resources. Raw materials, components, tools, and overhead expenses such as facilities are essential to many projects. As such, selecting, acquiring, and managing them involves a major effort, especially for the project manager. An even bigger, more unpredictable effort often goes toward acquiring and managing the *human resources*—the organizational staff members and outside contractors—needed to complete the project.

Of the three sides of the project triangle, resources can often be the most inflexible for several reasons:

- Contracts frequently dictate the exact amount of capital available.
- Human resources are often assigned at the beginning of the project, which gives the project leader little flexibility and few options for change.
- Resources most directly tied to an organization's "bottom line," or profitability, and thus, carry a host of expectations and implications that can complicate

the balance between "what's best" for the team and "what's best" for the organization.

- A delayed delivery date (*schedule*, one of the other sides of the triangle) is often more readily available than more resources (capital, materials, or team members).

Though managing project resources is vital as the project is in progress, there are also long-term effects to consider: are savings during the project going to cost more in the long run? Will decisions we make now have negative repercussions down the line? This concept, known as *life cycle cost analysis*, forces project-minded teams to consider the operational implications of their work, looking past their own budgets towards the good of the organization or customer. As an example, modularity may take more time to design and be more complex to build, but the ability to swap parts or upgrade components individually could mean significant cost savings in the long run.

What About Budgets and Procurement?
Though these activities are extremely important and can take up a significant part of a team leader's time, well-established standards and procedures in the areas of accounting and finance are almost outside of the leader's control, set instead by their organization. Additionally, many organizations have pre-established sources of material and/or provide all resources to project leaders at the start of the project. Because of this, more focus is placed on the decision making aspects rather than the mechanics of these particular project activities.

As stated above, human resources are frequently the most difficult type of resource to manage, often monopolizing the team leader's time. For example, in functional or matrix organizations the project leader can spend a significant amount of time mining the skillsets their project needs from an existing pool of resources, and even more time conversing with functional managers, seeking appropriate percentages of their resources time, and coordinating with other projects and operational work to which that resource is assigned. This, in turn, affects how a leader must prioritize their time. Further discussion regarding how to manage human resources is covered in other chapters of this book: General leadership is covered in chapter 1; team development and management is the focus of chapter 4; communication with the team as well as external stakeholders is covered in chapter 5; pitfalls that a team might encounter are listed in chapter 6.

Schedule

Schedule refers to the time it takes to plan, execute, and complete a project. The modern economy and resulting pace of business has put a great deal of emphasis on ever-tightening timescales. Because determining, managing, and tracking schedules is so important to project leadership, a significant portion of chapter 3 is dedicated to understanding how to properly create reasonable and sustainable schedules.

For many, schedule seems to be the most flexible aspect of the project triangle—they feel that if they can just work more efficient, longer hours, or even find shortcuts, they can shorten the time needed to complete a project, all without affecting the other sides of the triangle. It's important for project leaders to resist this temptation, especially in the long term. This is because an unsustainable pace can result in more waste, burnout-related mistakes, and loss of morale, leading to lower quality work and the exodus of much-needed personnel (see *Death March* on page 184).

Another factor, schedule compression, also called "fast-tracking" or "crashing," invariably comes at a cost to resources or quality. When team members are added to a project, they must be trained (at additional cost) and, for some period of time, won't work as efficiently as preexisting members. Additionally, more time or resources are needed to coordinate and communicate with the larger team and in turn, this faster pace taxes external dependencies such as contractors or materials providers. If other methods are employed, they also come at a cost. Consider, for example, how having materials shipped overnight is significantly more expensive than slower alternatives. Project managers must weigh this decision with the hard reality that additional time cannot be added to the 24-hour day.

The most practical way to shorten a project's schedule is to directly address one of the other sides of the triangle. More resources can be expended—hiring more experienced team members, for example, often results in quicker results with fewer errors (which themselves require schedule-extending rework). In addition, decreasing scope, the third side of the triangle, is often the easiest and most practical way to decrease schedule. Finally, placing lower-priority components near the end of the schedule makes for natural selection of the most vital elements should a looming deadline or shortened schedule become a reality. Employing cyclical or change-focused processes models make this much easier, since they are often iterative in nature.

Blurring the Line Between Resources and Schedule?
Many projects, especially those providing services or non-physical products such as software or written material, begin and end with the same

team and don't incur many non-labor costs as the project continues. In these situations, "time is money," since hours worked is essentially the only expense incurred by the project. Because of this, managing team coordination and the tasks individuals are completing becomes even more important, since the leader is now affecting two sides of the project triangle simultaneously.

Scope

The term *scope* refers to what is and isn't included in the project—the results to be created as the resources and schedule are consumed. Put another way, scope is the output(s) of the effort expended while implementing the project. What most immediately comes to mind is a product or service, though scope could also include other elements such as documentation, training, or future support, which are known as project *deliverables*. Deliverables are simply the products, services, or results that a project is intended to produce, but they aren't always delivered at the end of the project—they can be produced as the project is implemented. Scope and the deliverables that define it are always a planned, intentional result of the project.

Many equate the concept of quality directly with scope (some even label "scope" as "quality"). Quality, covered earlier in this section, has a foundation built of standards, conformance, and excellence; each of these considerations can be applied just as readily to schedule and resource management as to the scope of the project. Since considerations of quality should be at the center of all project activities, it's placed at the center of the project triangle, not at its edges.

The nature of the project triangle means that scope is often involved in trade-offs with schedule and resources. Because what is to be delivered by projects varies so wildly, there's not much more to be said about individual projects' scopes except this: it is important to spend time properly defining with little uncertainty what the scope of a project entails. This is the subject of the next section.

Scope Creep
One of the pitfalls covered in chapter 6 (page 187), "scope creep" represents the slow but meaningful expansion of a project's scope. Because of the constraints of the project triangle, scope creep inevitably leads to a longer schedule, the need for more resources, or both.

2.5 Defining Project Outcomes: A Layered Approach

Anyone who has participated in project work has heard terms thrown around which pertain to the outcomes of the project. These often include goals, objectives, scope, requirements, designs, and specifications. Though sometimes used interchangeably, these terms are, in fact, different in how each describes the work to be done. Because of this, using a layered approach (using the terms together in appropriate combinations), can provide a more complete picture of the project as it progresses from the planning stages onward. Before discussing this, we must first define the terms.

Goals

Goals, often written just as a project is starting, are statements that provide a context for what the project is trying to achieve. They have the following features:

- **High-level:** Goals provide a view of what the project is trying to achieve without necessarily specifying the specific products or actions needed to achieve them. Because goals are high-level, more specific descriptions of project outcomes are needed. Scope statements and requirements/specifications further clarify the project work needed to achieve these goals.

- **Measurable:** Though high-level descriptions may seem incompatible with the idea of measurement, goals should be defined (and more specifically, worded) so that it's clear when they have been accomplished. Ambiguity in this area may lead to out-of-control costs or schedules, or may indicate operational (non-project) work.

- **Reasonable:** It's important that goals have self-imposed limits since it's easy to set goals that are too lofty. Because of this, goals must conform to the capabilities of the time and resources allotted to the team (as well as the organization). This doesn't mean that they can't be challenging—they just need to be reasonably achievable.

  Some projects employ what are called "stretch goals." These are known to be somewhat beyond the normal expectations of the project but, provided the resources and/or time are available, could add additional value to the problem or need the project is designed to address. Improperly executed, stretch goals can have a negative effect on the project and the morale of the team (see *Scope Creep* on page 187).

- **Cross-compatible:** Goals must be compatible with each other as well as the mission and objectives of the organization. If goals are created that seem incompatible, more time must be dedicated to sorting out these inconsistencies; not doing so will most likely have disastrous consequences as the project progresses.

The type of language used in describing goals and the number of goals assigned to a project will vary based on the type of project as well as what it is trying to accomplish. Here are a few sample (unrelated to each other) goal statements:

- Increase pedestrian access to the B-line subway by 50%

- Setup the initial production line for the VS-400

- Explore the possibility of chemical SST-30 catalyzing the DKE-15 thermal reaction

- Expand the website to allow customers to pay via gift card

- Create a connection platform that will allow RB-8 tractors to power the HST-4 jackhammer

- Obtain funding for the organization's planned expansion to take place in the next fiscal year

- Install a well that will provide potable drinking water for 300 residents

- Increase corporate brand recognition by German 18-24 year-olds by 15%

- Come up with a unique, marketable name for product XRB-40

From the perspective of the project leader and team, goals serve as a kind of contract: in order for the project to be called "complete," its goals must be clearly met. Because of this, defining goals is usually one of the first project activities that take place, in some cases happening even before the project leader or manager has been chosen. (The project sponsor may define the goals when the project charter is created.) Goals which do not include numerical or black-and-white indicators need to be clarified. Often the first responsibility of a project leader is obtaining a clear understanding of the goals, their context, and what would constitute their completion. The prudent project leader then goes on to ensure that these clarifications are recorded and agreed upon by important stakeholders.

What About "Objectives"?

Objectives are related to goals; as such, the words are sometimes used interchangeably. Objectives describe what the planned outcomes of your project are in more concrete terms. Goals are somewhat more abstract, whereas objectives tend to be more exact. As discussed in the first part of this chapter, projects must be unique and time-limited, and their goals and objectives (as well as scope statements, requirements, and specifications) must follow that same pattern.

As the name implies, goals mark the beginning, or the most abstract element of defining what a project requires. Scope statements and requirements/specifications are increasingly more exact, and therefore demand increased effort in defining what they are to be.

Scope Statements

Scope statements are less abstract than goals or objectives; they more specifically spell out what is and isn't to be included in the project. Simply put, the scope statement defines the boundaries of the project—other terms that could be used here are "reach," "breadth," or "confines."

"Scope" vs. "Scope Statements"

In the previous section, the word "scope" (one side of the project triangle) is defined as *what is and isn't included in the project*. The "scope statement" formally defines this for a particular project and is typically in paragraph or list form. By declaring a project's scope, you are "solidifying" that side of the project triangle—leaving the task of defining necessary resources and schedule as separate work.

You'll notice that in addition to what is included, the definition of "scope" also specifies what *isn't* included in the project. This can be a little trickier to define, but it helps to think about what reasonable people (different stakeholder groups such as management or customers) might falsely assume is a part of the project. As you draft scope statements, you can also think about what these groups might intentionally add to a project that should not be there. This problem, known as *scope creep*, is an all-too-common and is perpetuated by both stakeholders and the core team (see *Scope Creep* on page 187). Intentionally defining what is not part of the project puts all of this strictly out-of-bounds.

As with goals, it should be reasonably easy for someone involved with the project to determine if the project outcomes included in the scope statement have been achieved—and if any work has been done outside of the its limits. A solidly written scope statement includes the following features:

- **A list of all major deliverables:** As covered in the last section, deliverables are simply the products, services, or results that a project is intended to produce. The scope statement should, with as little ambiguity as possible, list the important parts of the project's intended output.

- **A basic strategy:** This implies the high-level steps needed to achieve the project's goals and create its deliverables. Though the details will be worked out later, defining these in the scope statement begins to delineate the project as a structured solution to the problem it was initiated to address.

The Problem Statement

When defining the scope, many project teams start by carefully re-examining the problem or need the project is to address, often rewriting it as an introduction to the scope statement. This can be extremely helpful by providing context to readers of the scope; in short, choosing to include a problem statement with the scope statement is a commonly held "best practice."

- **Constraints:** Those reading the scope statement should have no problem understanding the limit of what is to be produced. An out-of-control scope results in out-of-control budgets and schedules. Some scope statements include a short section explaining the rationale for what is and isn't to be included in the project.

- **External dependencies:** Does your project depend on variables outside your control? If possible, define these as conditions or limitations in your scope statement.

- **Assumptions:** Similar to dependencies, is it possible that you are making assumptions about things like the availability of resources or information?

Assumptions are acceptable as long as they are explicitly defined, realistic, and agreed upon by all parties.

Though some projects try to break things down into a single sentence or statement, a proper scope statement often requires multiple paragraphs or, at the very least, a series of "bulleted" statements. The following sample scope statements include basic but clear descriptions of what is and isn't to be included in their associated projects:

Project: E-Flipper Marketing Campaign
Scope Statement: This project includes the initial marketing effort for the E-Flipper BBQ accessory within the themes and ideas presented in the initial proposal meeting. This includes the creation of:

- three different single-page advertisements
- one 15-second television commercial
- 6 variously-sized website banners with similar content (sizes to be determined by the client)

After approval, project will deliver screen or camera-ready, high-resolution digital files of each media item via secure file-transfer protocol. Files will be available for 30 days after approval.

Initial designs will be shared and approved by the client, with up to 3 revisions per media item before completion of refined final product. Additional revisions or extension of ideas would be out of scope, requiring a separate contract and project. Project does not include assistance in placement of advertising media, future modifications, or retrieval of files after 30 days.

Project: BitBoop App 1.0
Scope Statement: This project is intended to create the first version of the BitBoop App including basic user profiles and basic features. User profile functionality will include basic login, logout, and persistent profile information via the Goofle API. Basic features will include the ability to post photos and attach pre-selected sound effects to them and the ability to view the photos and sound effects of others based on username. Initially, the application will support up to 50,000 simultaneous users.

Functionality beyond what is described above, whether planned or unplanned, will not be included in this project. This includes user profiles involving other API's (such as Amazor). The ability to delete posts, post private photos, "like," or "follow" are examples of planned functionality that are not a part of the BitBoop App 1.0 project.

Project: PartCo RX-58 Installation

Scope Statement: This project will include installation, testing, and on-site training of the RX-58 stamping machine within PartCo's Springtown manufacturing facility.

The project will not include electrical tie-in beyond an in-place power box, integration of the machine with upstream or downstream machines or processes, testing beyond basic functionality, training after the date of installation, or training for more than 10 employees of PartCo.

Project: East Ave Hydrant Repair Project

Scope Statement: Last month's extensive ice damage has necessitated repair or replacement of several fire hydrants in the 400-block of East Ave. This project is designed to evaluate and repair damage to this vital system and to restore proper, code complaint active fire protection to this region. Parties expected to be engaged in this project include the city code department, fire commission, and county road construction crews.

This project will not include replacement, relocation, or augmentation of any hydrants unless deemed necessary by the code inspector, likely due to conditions that are unsafe or will lead to repetition of the original problem. In most cases, this is expected to result in continued use of existing hydrants, valves, pipes, and connections.

Note that each of these explicitly states any necessary deliverables and includes elements such as problem definitions, constraints, external dependencies, or assumptions when necessary. A properly crafted scope statement takes reasonable steps to avoid as much opportunity for ambiguity or misinterpretation as is practical.

Schedule Before Scope?

Some organizations prefer scope statements to include not just what is to be completed, but also the deadlines, schedules, or statements regarding level of effort and resources that will contribute the process. If these things must be included, the team must complete formal estimation and scheduling efforts before committing to a final scope statement (see *Estimation Methods* on page 80 and *Project Scheduling* on page 88).

Finally, though the scope statement is designed to place limits on the breadth of what a project is to include, it does little to address the depth of details needed to properly engage and execute a project. This depth, a further reduction in the abstraction of description, is typically defined in requirements or specifications.

Requirements and Specifications

Requirements and specifications clearly state what your project aims to achieve. They are intended to span not only the product or solution your project is to create (often called "functional" requirements or specifications) but can also include other limits or needs placed on your project ("non-functional"), such as schedule and budget restrictions and less-definable qualitative elements such as safety, documentation, usability, aesthetics, and compatibility with expectations about the future. There should be no room for abstract generalizations—requirements and specifications are written so that anyone reading them knows exactly what should be achieved in the execution phase of the project.

The language of requirements or specifications often differs from the general vernacular and favors specificity, as illustrated in the following examples:

- All user-accessible web pages shall render properly on the latest major version of each of the top three mobile browsers

- All samples provided for testing require a concentration of 100ng/ul

- Training personnel shall be approved by the regional operations manager of the facility at which they are to enter and are subject to search before entry

- The product in its entirety is to be delivered 45 business days after the Statement of Work is signed

- The exterior dimensions of the box shall be 30 units wide by 22 units long by 12 units high with interior dimensions of at least 29.75 units wide by 21.75 units long by 11.75 units high

- All beta-level priority service interruptions will receive a documented response within 3 business hours and a response plan within 12 business hours

- The secondary module casing shall be produced using 0.3 thick 304 grade stainless steel

The process for collecting or authoring these requirements or specifications is an undertaking that varies by industry, organization, and project. Indeed, large projects may have an entire sub-project which spans months and whose primarily deliverable is a requirements/specifications document. In some cases the specifications or requirements are dictated by the customer or stakeholders for which the project is intended. In others, experts or members of the team are the ones who write them. No matter who authors them, all parties must agree that the requirements or specifications represent precisely what the project is to deliver.

Because one party is often better informed and because the use of technical jargon or scientific measurement is often required, agreeing on the requirements and specifications for a project almost always requires a relationship of mutual trust between the team and those for whom the project will be completed. In some cases, project requirements/specifications entail the most essential part of the contract signed by both parties. In others, defining them represents the first significant interaction between the team and the customer in the beginning phases of the project.

In addition to serving as a guide during project execution, requirements and specifications can be used when the schedule or budget poses a significant restriction to the project. Once a list has been compiled, the team and stakeholders can then prioritize its items, choosing which are the most important and should to be completed first. This allows for a "minimum viable" solution to be created, with additional work to be done as time or resources become available. This technique is commonly employed by teams using cyclical or change-focused process models (covered on pages 38 and 40).

It should be noted that the techniques and practices behind defining requirements and specifications entail a rather large discipline—universities teach entire classes on the subject and entire books are written about the practices and approaches involved. Requirements and specifications have an undeniable connection to a project's quality, which was covered in the previous section of this chapter.

The Layered Approach

How do goals, scope statements, and requirements/specifications work to advance the project? Using them properly requires you to understand their commonalities and overarching objectives as you define project outcomes:

1. To gain understanding and approval from essential stakeholders, and

2. to gain enough information and clarification for the team to begin executing the work.

Both of these are focused on ensuring that the people involved with the project know how the proposed solution is intended to meet the original problem or need. Essentially, the team needs to add "layers" one at a time, stopping when they achieve an appropriate level of understanding. By proceeding deliberately and checking frequently, you can optimize level of detail against the effort required in this step. This level of detail or specificity varies from project-to-project and team-to-team, as do the specific "layers" needed.

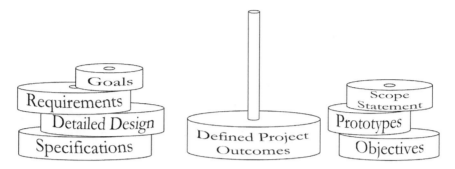

Extra Layers?

Some projects require even deeper levels of information or planning to proceed, especially if they are to achieve the goals of understanding, approval, and readiness required to start production. Examples of this could include detailed design documents, specialized drawings, proofs of concept, or prototypes. By specifying in even more exacting terms what is to be created, the team can proceed more confident that they are all on the same page, and that their solution is more likely to meet the project's goals.

So how do we determine which of these "layers" are needed? The answer lies in the following considerations:

- **There is a minimum:** Most professionals would agree that at bare minimum, projects should have a scope statement and defined goals/objectives. Small projects with teams that have completed similar work in the past may find this level of definition adequate, but at least one more layer of specificity is typically needed (usually in the form of requirements/specifications).

- **They build upon each other:** Each of these layers has a relationship with the others. For example, goals are addressed by scope statements, which are described by requirements or specifications.

- **They are often industry or organization specific:** In some cases, the differences are in name only; in others, there is a real difference between the preferences of different industries. Occasionally, regulations require specific formats; building codes and financial statements are examples of this. Sometimes entirely different documents are used (blueprints, technical spec sheets, etc.).

In addition to *which* layers are needed, the project team must consider *the order* in which the layers should be added. For example, if a scope statement and requirements/specifications are needed, which should be completed first?

A project that has been more-or-less defined before it's started often places defining the scope before requirements or specifications. Scope is set by the sponsor or a contract with the customer, and stakeholders (often the customer themselves) are consulted to work out the level of detail required before the team can create the requirements or specifications. If the stakeholder asks for something outside the previously defined scope, it is politely refused or considered as an addition to the project's baseline scope before acceptance. This type of practice prevents undue expansion of the project and favors the expertise of the team over that of stakeholders.

If the project hasn't been previously well-defined, gathering requirements and/or writing specifications often takes place first, with a scope statement completed soon after. Stakeholders' needs and direct input are considered (as requirements or specifications) and that input becomes the basis for the project's scope statement. This method tends to favor the expertise of stakeholders, with team members relying on them to properly understand both the problem and their opinion of what a project-based solution would look like (its scope).

Both of these examples are heavily influenced by factors such as industry norms, the common practices of the organization, and the analysis of the stakeholders themselves (see *Chapter Tool: Prioritizing Stakeholders* on page 102).

Predictive or Reactive Problem Solving?

The paragraphs above present scenarios in which it makes more sense to write either the scope or the requirements/specifications first. At their core, these differences are a result of the general approach needed to address the "project problem." *Predictive problem solving* seeks to solve problems that haven't yet occurred or tries to predict future markets. *Reactive problem solving* addresses problems or opportunities that have already occurred. Both scenarios are best addressed with a layered approach, but each might dictate differences in the order in which "layers" are completed.

Regardless of order, project outcomes aren't properly defined until each appropriate layer has been written and added. But when are these written? The next section discusses the project's early phases, which include the creation of a *project plan* document that includes the defined outcomes.

2.6 The Project's Early Stages

Projects, by their very nature, are unique. Because of this, the steps performed along the way can vary quite widely, and are further complicated by variations in how individual organizations conduct work. Once begun, a project follows a planned life cycle that includes early, middle, and late (concluding) stages. During this life cycle, project stages can vary based on the focus of the organization and the process it chooses to employ (plan-focused, cyclical, or change-focused). A project's conclusion, its closing stage, represents the unique result the project was intended to deliver.

Although the way a project starts can vary widely in different organizations, there are two elements that many project inceptions have in common: the *project kickoff meeting* and the *project plan* document.

The Project Kickoff Meeting

You've been chosen as the project's leader; you've met with the project sponsor, reviewed the project charter, and figured out who's on the core project team. You have a clear understanding of why the project is important and even a few ideas about how you'd like to reach the objectives before you. It's time for a project kickoff meeting.

Because the kickoff meeting represents the first impression of the project and its team for many attendees, it's important that it be organized, relevant, and well-executed. A well-thought-out meeting agenda should be prepared to include the majority of the objectives laid out above. Key stakeholders such as important team members, the project sponsor, and the customer (if applicable) should be present. Though a face-to-face meeting is preferable, the use of online conferencing tools may be a viable option. In some cases, a separate meeting for the customer may be appropriate, especially if their role in each step of the project will be limited.

For many team members and stakeholders, the project kickoff meeting is their first view of the project. This meeting is intended to:

- Establish the project as a unique, time-limited effort, distinguishing it from any other projects or operational work in progress

- Share high-level objectives and goals, which ensures that attendees understand why the project is important

- Build awareness, enthusiasm, and support for the project in the minds of the team and stakeholders

- Introduce team members to each other and promote cooperation and communication—the members of the project team will probably be working together for an extensive period of time

- Define team member roles and responsibilities

- Communicate processes and methods the team will use; by establishing these up front, everyone will clearly understand future work and documentation expectations

- Choose regular team-meeting times

- Establish a common set of tools; these can relate to a product or service directly, but also to practical decisions such as where project documents will "live" and the preferred methods of communication to be used

- Define what success means to the project and its team

- Begin some foundational work—start planning the project. This usually means writing a high-level project plan (covered below). Many of its sections can be written as an outline or with few specifics, then enhanced with more detail as the effort continues

Meeting Success

Good meetings can be extremely effective, but to many employees, meetings carry a reputation as a disorganized, irrelevant waste of time. Chapter 3 includes a section on how to avoid common meeting mistakes and increase the likelihood of successful project meetings (see page 159).

Once the kickoff meeting is complete, the project leader should follow up with a communication thanking attendees for being there, reinforcing what was covered by the meeting, along with information, decisions, and actions that arose from the meeting itself. At this point, most projects begin to work on creating the project plan.

Phase Kickoff Meetings?
What about large multi-year projects—is one kickoff meeting enough? In this case, it may be prudent to consider kickoff meetings at the beginning of each major project phase. These meetings give the team an opportunity to celebrate their achievements (from the previous phase), reconnect with far-flung teammates, and build excitement for the phases to come.

The Project Plan

The single largest pre-execution effort in most projects is the creation of the project plan. This *artifact* documents the results of the initiation and planning phases of the project and brings it to the precipice of execution. Though it may seem daunting, it allows the leader and team to think through the project, plan it out, and document the decisions and information as they become available. Later in the project, the project plan becomes a valuable tool that helps provide understanding to stakeholders and assists in bringing new team members up to speed.

Why the Term "Artifact"?
You've heard of historical artifacts, but why *project artifacts*? Finding pottery from an ancient culture tells you much more than "they made pottery"—it contains information about materials available, levels of technological development, and cultural exchanges with others nearby. Similarly, project artifacts allow individuals during and after-the-fact to ascertain information about the team, the resources and time available, and the status of the project.

Though it may vary from project-to-project, a typical project plan has the following components:

1. **An executive summary:** Limited to one page or less, this serves to quickly explain the basic why, what, who, when, and how to the reader. By reading this single page, someone can acquire a general understanding of the project:

- Why has the project been initiated?
- What is the project supposed to accomplish? What are its main outcomes?
- Who, at the highest levels, are the project's major stakeholders?
- When is it supposed to begin and end? What are the major stops along the way?
- How, in a brief description, is it to be accomplished?

Note that although it's the first page of the document, it's typically one of the last written.

Project Plan: Executive Summary
This is written after the completion of most planning and the rest of the document.
Components/Sections: A single page summary with input from the project charter (see *The Project Charter and the Project Sponsor* on page 26) and other sections of the project plan.

References to Other Chapters
Because this project plan description is an outline, the following sections reference other chapters quite heavily. Because of this, you may need to revisit this section after reading chapter 3—doing so should clarify what an actual project plan may look like.

2. **Appropriately detailed outcomes:** This includes as many of the "layers" as needed to properly define the project outcomes (covered in the last section, starting on page 58). Examples include goals, objectives, scope statements, requirements, and specifications, and each warrants its own sub-heading. Remember that the elements required to appropriately define your project outcomes may vary. This section is typically written first, starting with the most abstract sections (objectives, goals, and deliverables) moving toward more exacting details (scope statements, requirements, etc.).

Project Plan: Project Outcomes
Typically written first, with revisions as needed.
Components/Sections:
- Goals and/or Objectives (see *Goals* on page 51)
- Scope Statement: Includes what is and isn't part of the project (see *Scope Statements* on page 53).

- Requirements and/or Specifications: Often listed as a table or bullets (see *Requirements and Specifications* on page 57).
- Work Breakdown Structure: An organized breakdown of the work to be done (see *The Work Breakdown Structure* on page 88).
- Project Deliverables: A listing of what's to be created by the project (defined on page 50).

3. **Schedule and budget information:** Typically written after defining the project's planned outcomes, this section lays out the expected schedule and budget information for the project. If significant materials or resources are needed to execute the project, information on how to choose and procure these items would also be included here. If any significant changes are made to the schedule or budget, revisions need to be made to this section as well. Note that estimation, scheduling, and budgeting efforts represent a significant effort by the team.

Project Plan: Schedule and Budget
Written after the Project Outcomes section and major estimation, scheduling, and budgeting efforts have been completed.
Components/Sections:
- Milestones: Major scheduling milestones (see *Visualizing the Schedule* on page 91).
- Schedule: Built through estimation and scheduling efforts (a major focus of chapter 3).
- Budget: Financial information related to the project. Often governed by the organization's policies and procedures.
- Procurement Plan: A plan for resources or services that are to be acquired in the course of the project.
- Dependencies: Internal and external resources or events that are needed for the schedule and budget to be valid.

4. **A resource and process management plan:** This section establishes who and what the project's resources are and how they are going to be organized. The process and change-management-related sections are often well established by previous projects—they can often be readily copied and modified.

Project Plan: Resource and Process Management
Added to and updated as the plans are made.
Components/Sections:

- Human Resource Management: A listing of the project's team members and external human resources, their reporting structure, and their responsibilities. A RASCI is an appropriate tool here (see *The "RASCI" Accountability Matrix* on page 136).
- Project Resource Management: A listing of the non-human resources available to the project and how they are to be managed.
- Processes and Change Procedures: This references or lists the processes that the team will follow in each phase of the project or when making major changes to schedules or budgets (see *Values, Needs, and Process* on page 36).

5. **How quality is addressed:** Defining up-front how your project is going to address both process and product quality ensures that team members and stakeholders have proper expectations in this area. This chapter's tool, entitled *Chapter Tool: Planning Project Quality* (page 69) provides some basic instruction for helping a project team get started.

Project Plan: Quality Assurance Plan
Written after sections listed above (except the Executive Summary) are completed.
Components/Sections:

- Process Quality
    - Standard Procedures: Often previously defined by the organization or team (see *Quality and The Project Triangle* on page 43).
    - Artifacts to be Created: Should include approval or review procedures needed for each.
    - Process Review and Improvement Plan: Related to a project's *Lessons Learned*, covered on page 170.
- Product Quality
    - Quality Specifications: Clearly specified tests or standards to be met (conforming to explicitly defined quality elements, described on page 44).
    - Quality Focus: The implicit focus of quality efforts—the quality-related goals the project hopes to achieve (see *Excellence* on page 44).

6. **Stakeholder analysis and communication planning:** It's important to define who the project's stakeholders are and the team's plans for communicating important project information to them at regular intervals.

Project Plan: Stakeholder Communication Plan
Updated regularly throughout the planning process.
Components/Sections:

- Stakeholder Register: A table containing a list of all individuals or groups who can affect or are affected by the project (building a proper stakeholder register is described in the next chapter (page 103).
- Communication Plan: A communication plan should include the following information:
  - What: The type of information to be communicated. Examples include status updates (such as the Quad Chart, covered on page 173) and reports (covered on page 164).
  - How: The method, or channel, of delivery (see *Channels of Communication* on page 151).
  - To Whom: The recipients of each type of communication. These should line up with the stakeholders identified in your stakeholder register.
  - When: Information about the frequency of communication or specific scenarios that would trigger a communique. This relates to the idea of *Expectation Management*, covered on page 171.
  - Who: The team members or roles responsible for conducting the communication. Different team structures (covered on page 114) will handle this differently.

7. **Consideration of risks and issues:** Though we hope for ideal conditions and predictable results, it's important for the project team to consider situations where the project faces delays, shortages, or other negative conditions. This section creates a place to list issues, seeks out potential risks, and establishes procedures for addressing these issues and risks.

Project Plan: Risk and Issue Management
This is written as potential issues and risks are encountered; these are often discovered as other parts of the project plan are authored.

Components/Sections:

- Initial Risk and Issue Analysis: SWOT analysis is an appropriate tool to help with this (see page 98).
- Risk Register: Establishment of a risk table which should be revisited frequently throughout the project (for an example, see page 101).
- Issue List: Often tracked electronically. Includes issue names, details, and resources assigned to resolving them.
- Risk and Issue Procedures: Establishment of procedures for identifying, recording, and working thorough issues and risks. These will often heavily rely on documented organizational processes and procedures.

8. **Appropriate approval and revision information:** Plans, and the artifacts that document them, are subject to change and revision and must be visible to important parties. Establishing a set of procedures for managing important changes to the project minimizes the chance of surprised stakeholders and failed project objectives. Including a revision log can clarify which version of the document a stakeholder has. In addition, including approval information specifies which parties must formally review and sign-off on the plan.

Project Plan: Document Revision and Approval
Written when the document is established; revised as changes are made to the document or approval is received.
Components/Sections:

- Change Procedures: The procedures that should be followed when making major changes to the project's deliverables, schedule, or budget.
- Revision History: A log of major changes listing revision details, which includes authors and dates. This may be created electronically (see *The Modern Project Manager* on page 17).
- Approval: Proof of plan acceptance by appropriate parties, which, in some cases, may include physical signatures.

Though many project teams choose to organize the project plan as a single document, it may be more appropriate to use an organized collection of documents which, stored together, are independently updated as needed. Maintaining formal project documentation such as a project plan has several benefits:

- It allows the transfer of official information between parties (such as new team members).

- Recording project information can help prevent the absence of one person becoming a single point of failure.

- Documentation forces the team to consider what they are doing and puts it into context.

- Recording decisions and information can help to prevent re-work.

- Achieving quality results can be a moving target, and documentation can help to stabilize efforts.

- Some customers include documentation standards and favor organizations that follow them (see *ISO 9001 Certification* on page 43).

- Information about successes, failures, estimates, etc. can be useful to future projects (see *Lessons Learned* on page 170).

Ultimately the documentation your team chooses to create should be based on organizational policies, customer preferences, and the team's needs. Each artifact should fulfill a purpose, the importance of which should be known to the team as they work to create it. If an artifact's value isn't apparent, it may be prudent to discontinue its use or modify it to meet the needs of the project.

2.7 Chapter Tool: Planning Project Quality

The concept of quality and how it applies to work seems quite daunting at times. With so many aspects, all of which seem important, it can be difficult to get started. As the project progresses, applying those concepts, tracking how well the team is doing, and making decisions can be just as difficult. This chapter tool gives you a basic method for prioritizing the most important aspects of quality as you plan and execute your project.

Exercising Quality

As you read through the steps that follow, think about a project you've worked on in the past. On a piece of paper, complete steps 1-4 as best as you remember. Once this is complete, think about steps 5 and 6— did your project team properly consider the most important aspects of quality as the project continued and neared completion?

Complete each of the following basic steps in order:

1. **Choose 4-6 aspects of quality that are most important to your project. Choose equal numbers from each category (product and process quality):** If two aspects seem very similar, choose only the one that seems more important within the context of your organization and what your project is trying to achieve. Note that this is far from an exhaustive list, so feel free to choose other aspects of quality relevant to your project. Many of these aspects are related to the organizational values and project needs discussed on page 36.

Product Quality	Process Quality
Features	Perception
Performance	Timeliness
Efficiency	Cost Efficiency
Durability	Process Improvement
Reliability	Safety
Serviceability	Stakeholder Relationships
Aesthetics	Precision of Execution
Uniformity	Approval
Availability	Compliance
Resource Consumption	Responsiveness

2. **Rank the chosen aspects above from most important to least important:** If two seem just as important as each other, then place them side-by-side. As you do this, you should get a sense of which aspects emerge as more essential than others and should help you dismiss the less prominent aspects.

3. **Distribute 20 "importance" points between them:** This converts your ranked list into one with individual weights of importance. An example could look like this:

Quality Aspect	Points
Stakeholder Relationships	5
Approval	4
Cost Efficiency	4
Features	3
Aesthetics	2
Reliability	2
Total	**20**

4. **Use a "radar chart" to visualize the balance of prioritization:** This chart should be divided into product and process quality. Using spreadsheet

software or online tools makes this much easier than using pen-and-paper. Here's an example representing the same values from the previous table:

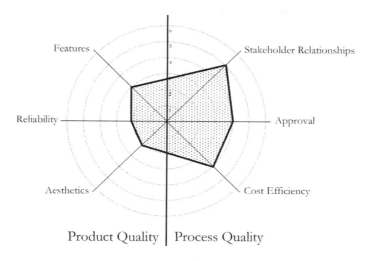

5. **Analyze the balance between product quality and process quality:** If one side appears "heavier," this could indicate that, given limited resources, more attention should be expended planning and tracking related areas of focus.

Product quality may require, for example:

- Properly defining project outcomes such as the scope statement and requirements (see *Defining Project Outcomes: A Layered Approach* on page 51).

- A schedule and resource focus on product-related standards, conformance, and excellence (see *Quality and The Project Triangle* on page 43).

- Including product testing and verification activities in your schedule (see *Project Scheduling* on page 88).

- Placing special emphasis on risks that affect the quality of the end product (see *Risk Management* on page 97).

- Focusing keenly on results as a team (see *Focusing on Results* on page 138)

- Paying special attention to pitfalls such as *Fire Drill* (page 185) and *Rushing to Execution* (page 186).

- Organization or industry-specific product quality standards and expectations.

Process quality may require, for example:

- A solid understanding of how the organizational environment affects your processes (see *The Project Environment* on page 30).

- A focus on defining and refining your process (see *Values, Needs, and Process* on page 36).

- Including time in your schedule to review and improve your process; prescheduling regular meetings on the topic can help with this.

- Ensuring proper communication with internal and external stakeholders (the topic of chapter 5).

- Spending more time seeking process-related risks (see *Risk Management* on page 97).

- Watching out for common pitfalls such as *Analysis Paralysis* (page 184) and *Death March* (page 184).

- Organization or industry-specific standards and expectations regarding how projects are carried out.

A more balanced radar chart requires you to adopt a holistic approach, considering both product and process quality carefully.

6. **Review quality priorities at each step of the project:** As work continues, it can be easy for individuals to forget which aspects of a project are most important. By constantly refocusing on the aspects of quality that are most important, the team is less likely to get "off track." One way to avoid this is to place the radar chart in a prominent, visible location in the office, which ensures that all team members involved in the project can regularly see the aspects of highest priority.

The 7 Quality Tools

First listed by Kaoru Ishikawa,[12] the 7 basic tools of quality provide a way to analyze quality issues *visually*. Though some choose to add additional tools to the list, Ishikawa 7 basic quality tools include: the cause-and-effect diagram, tally sheet, control chart, histogram, Pareto chart, scatter diagram, and statistical sampling. An online search will reveal numerous descriptions, examples, and uses of each.

2.8 Summary and Conclusion

It's important to remember that the ways a project is carried out can vary, with different organizational structures affecting how resources are allocated and values and needs affecting how the project's process is carried out. Therefore, understanding the nature of projects, their environment, and their progression are fundamentally important to planning and executing them successfully. What's more, a continuous balancing act occurs between the three elements of the project triangle (resources, schedule, and scope) and the various aspects of quality.

The early phases of a project are essential; this is where planned outcomes are documented in increasingly exact terms (goals, scope statements, and requirements/specifications, for example). Once a project kickoff meeting is held, the project team must then begin the planning process, which includes creating the project plan and considering abstract ideas like product and process quality assurance.

This chapter includes a fair amount on the early phases of a project, but may seem to stop short, offering little advice on the actual execution phase of a project. Because of the unique nature of organizations, industries, teams, and the projects themselves, this is left to the project leader—it's why they're needed, after all! The well-prepared project team does their best to plan appropriately, but all projects share two important features that help carry them to completion: the need for a variety of skills and an element of uncertainty. The remaining chapters of this book provide insight into planning, decision making, managing a team, and communication—all of which are core competencies required to face this uncertain future.

Key Terms

Artifact: Something created as part of a project that isn't the defined, intended end-product, service, or result. Often a document; contrasts with *deliverables* (page 63).

Best Practice: A procedure that is widely-accepted to be standardized, effective, or appropriate in most cases (page 44).

Business Need: A problem or opportunity that may result in the initiation of a project. Often identified by the *project sponsor* (page 25).

Cost of Poor Quality: Costs incurred due to inattention to quality during a project (such as rework and customer dissatisfaction). Balanced against *cost of quality* (page 45).

Cost of Quality: Quality-related costs incurred during a project (such as planning, research, and testing). Balanced against *cost of poor quality* (page 45).

Deliverables: The products, services, or results that a project is intended to produce. Contrasts with *artifacts* (page 50).

Execution: The *project life cycle* phase where plans are implemented, typically resulting in creation of the intended *deliverables* (page 27).

Functional Organization: An organizational structure defined by separate operational "silos." Projects are often assigned resources from one or more functional areas (page 31).

Goals (Project): High-level statements that serve to provide context for what the project is trying to achieve (page 51).

Matrix Organization: An organizational structure which has features of both a *functional organization* and a *project-focused organization* (page 34).

Operational Work: The ongoing, repetitive work within an organization, or "business as usual." Often contrasted with *projects* (page 26).

Process Model: An abstract representation of the steps completed in carrying out a project. Three basic categories focus on planning, cycles, and change (page 37).

Product Life Cycle: Related to marketing and production, the basic stages experienced by a product, including conception, growth, maturity, decline, and withdrawal (page 29).

Project: A planned, time-limited group of actions designed to achieve specific goals or outcomes. Contrasts with *operational work* (page 25).

Project Charter: A project *artifact* completed at the initiation of a new project, typically by the *project sponsor(s)*. It defines objectives, main stakeholders, and initial funding, giving the project leader authority to begin (page 25).

Project-Focused Organization: An organizational structure defined by resources' primary attachment to the project rather than individual departments. Often contrasted with *functional organizations* (page 33).

Project Functions: Project activities that generally require continuous monitoring and controlling. An element but not a phase of the *project life cycle* (page 28).

Project Life Cycle: The basic phases through which most projects pass. Includes conception/initiation, planning, *execution*, and closing (page 27).

Project Plan: An *artifact* typically completed early in the project defining important elements of the project and how it's to be carried out (page 63).

Project Sponsor: The individual or group who verifies the problem or opportunity to be addressed by the project. Often responsible for authoring the *project charter* and championing the project. A major stakeholder (page 25).

Project Triangle: A model defining the three constraints of a project: *scope*, resources, and schedule. Changes to one constraint requires adjustments to one or both remaining constraints (page 46).

Scope: What is and isn't to be included in the project, or its "boundaries." An element of the *project triangle* often expressed as a scope statement (page 50, 53).

Review Questions

1. In addition to a defined beginning and end, which other feature characterizes a project?

2. Who is responsible for identifying the problem or opportunity to be addressed by the project and often authors the project charter?

3. Which phase typically follows the planning phase in the project life cycle?

4. Name two project functions.

5. A project is assigned two resources from marketing, one from finance, and three from IT. Which type of organization does this likely represent?

6. Your project has solid require-

ments/specifications and an inexperienced team. Which category of process models is most appropriate?

7. Which element describing project outcomes focuses on stating what is and what isn't to be included in the project?

8. Which section of the project plan is usually written last?

Exercises

1. Until now the organization you work for has typically focused on operational factory production work. You've just been hired as a project manager to complete several important upgrades, and you're concerned about the "operational culture," which may not be compatible with project work. What strategies would you employ to improve your chances of success in these circumstances?

2. You've been tasked with overseeing the design, production, and marketing of a new type of hand-held media player. Name five projects that could be completed as part of this product's life cycle.

3. Project-focused organizations can experience negative effects when their projects compete for the limited resources available. In an environment that should focus on productivity, project leaders may find themselves "playing politics"—vying for attention in sometimes counterproductive ways. You've been promoted to VP of Projects and would like to prevent or alleviate some of these issues. Which strategies would you employ?

4. The organization you work for has traditionally used plan-focused processes when completing projects. Because your current customer often changes their mind on what they expect of you and your team, you're considering switching to a change-focused model. What are three potential advantages and three potential pitfalls of this decision?

5. The first phases of your design project have gone well, but the final version of the smoke detector you team has designed has failed a few required tests. Given what you know about the balance of quality and the project triangle, what are some possible implications of this new circumstance?

6. You're using the layered approach to define the outcome of a parking lot project for the local public high school. Write 3 goals/objectives, a scope statement

including what is and isn't a part of the project, and 3 specifications/requirements in line with this scenario.

7. The project sponsor has just chosen you to lead a new web-based software project. Create a basic agenda for the project's 2-hour kickoff meeting.

Notes

[1] Project Management Institute. *A Guide to the Project Management Body of Knowledge – Fifth Edition.* Project Management Institute Inc. p. 3. 2013.

[2] Project Management Institute. *A Guide to the Project Management Body of Knowledge – Fifth Edition.* Project Management Institute Inc. p. 42. 2013.

[3] Project Management Institute. *A Guide to the Project Management Body of Knowledge – Fifth Edition.* Project Management Institute Inc. p. 21-22. 2013.

[4] Project Management Institute. *A Guide to the Project Management Body of Knowledge – Fifth Edition.* Project Management Institute Inc. p. 10-12. 2013.

[5] *Development Cooperation Handbook.* https://en.wikibooks.org/wiki/Development_ Cooperation_Handbook/The_development_aid_organization/The_projectized_organization. Accessed September 2017.

[6] Project Management Institute. *A Guide to the Project Management Body of Knowledge – Fifth Edition.* Project Management Institute Inc. p. 44-46. 2013.

[7] International Organization for Standardization. *ISO 9000 - Quality management.* https://www.iso.org/iso-9001-quality-management.html. Retrieved 2017.

[8] David A. Garvin. *Competing on the eight dimensions of quality. Harvard Business review.* Harvard Business review November 1987.

[9] Crosby, P.B. *Completeness: Quality for the 21st century.* Plume. p. 45. 1992.

[10] Feigenbaum, Armand V. *Total Quality Control.* Harvard Business Review. p. 34. November 1956.

[11] Cunningham, Ward. *The WyCash Portfolio Management System.* OOPSLA'92. Vancouver. 1992.

[12] Ishikawa, Kaoru. *What Is Total Quality Control? The Japanese Way - First Edition,* Englewood Cliffs, New Jersey: Prentice-Hall, p. 198. 1985.

Prioritization: The Core of Project Leadership

Reviewing what they are trying to accomplish can leave a project team overwhelmed. In this chapter, we'll explore the concepts behind choosing priority: properly understanding how long tasks will take, ordering them properly, consistently and accurately evaluating risk and status, and analyzing the people important to the project.

The word "tasks" is deceptively simple. It implies that one only needs to complete a limited number of items to fulfill an objective. In reality, having more than one task highlights the importance of prioritization:

- Which task is more important?
- Can one task be started before another is completed?
- What if this is a really easy task... can we do it first?
- What about problems that arise—are they beyond our control?
- How do we report progress along the way?
- How do we even know that progress has been made?

3.1   Why is Prioritization So Essential?

By taking a systematic approach to answering the questions listed above, project leaders, team members, and managers can assert control over and increase the predictability of project results. First, to properly prioritize, adequate information must be ascertained about the work that needs to be done—this is achieved through estimation. Next, tasks and work units must be scheduled, and risks must be found and accounted for. Finally, during project execution, progress needs to be tracked, adjustments made, and status accurately reported. In each of these actions, the project team must *prioritize*, or make decisions, about what should come first, which tasks are more important, and, if needed, which parts of the project will not be completed before the deadline.

The remainder of this chapter takes the systematic approach outlined in the previous paragraph. Each section breaks down the processes that must be enacted and decisions that must be made to properly engage in project work. As you read, think about the prioritization—deciding when "this goes before that"—that is essential to each concept.

3.2   Estimation Methods

To develop a proper understanding of estimation, it's important to make distinctions based on levels of *granularity* that estimation can take. Early project activities such as strategic planning, feasibility studies, and contract negotiation require estimations of large blocks of deliverables—essentially the entire project needs to be estimated as accurately as possible. After the project has kicked off, it becomes necessary to estimate smaller units of work, usually down to the individual task, or, at the very least, down to a level that allows enough understanding to properly execute the work. Although the mechanics may differ slightly between estimating *time* and estimating *resources* (typically financial), many of the same methods can be used to create these estimates.

The following techniques are most commonly used:

Expert Judgement

This is the method that all others are built on. An "expert"— someone with previous experience—analyzes the situation and makes a determination resulting in an estimate.

- **Strengths:** Based on previous experience. Expert lends credibility to the estimate for stakeholders.
- **Weaknesses:** Because the estimate is potentially based on one (or more) people's expertise, a problem with their credibility may negatively reflect on the project as well.

- **Keys to Success:** Keeping good records, or "lessons learned" gives the expert proper perspective on past experiences. Because of this, they're consistently comparing previous estimates with actual results and using these previous comparisons to guide their current ones.

Top-Down Estimation

In top-down estimating, the expert or team determines the size of the whole unit, and then divides it into smaller and smaller chunks that sum into the ones above them, until all tasks/activities are small enough to be completed as separate units.

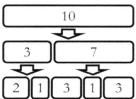

- **Strengths:** Useful when less detail is known about the final product. Some divided sections of a project are very similar to those of other projects, so consider using their actual results in such cases.
- **Weaknesses:** If major details are missed, the accuracy of this method suffers.
- **Keys to Success:** As more information is learned about a project, the team should revise their estimate in a similar top-down way.

Bottom-Up Estimation

In many ways the opposite of top-down, bottom-up first tries to consider all of the smallest tasks or work units and then sums them together to obtain a larger estimate.

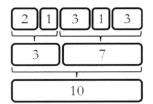

- **Strengths:** If individual activities are well known, this method may provide a more precise estimate.
- **Weaknesses:** This method can be more time consuming which may result in inefficiencies, especially if the project's activities are likely to change.
- **Keys to Success:** If individual activities, work units, or tasks have been completed before, use actual times whenever possible.

Comparison or Analogy Estimation

With this method, historical data is studied under the idea that previous projects with similar attributes will give insight into current estimates.

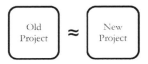

- **Strengths:** Because current estimates are based on actual historical data, they gain credibility with management and decision makers.

- **Weaknesses:** Projects are by their very nature unique, so finding candidates for comparison can be difficult. When differences are found, adjustments require additional consideration.
- **Keys to Success:** To compare projects appropriately, it's imperative to properly record data on actual times to completion and lessons learned. The success of future projects depends on proper documentation of current projects.

Group Consensus / Planning Poker Estimation

Using an established process, a facilitator helps the team reach a consensus estimate on a project, work unit, or activity. Typically, initial estimates are collected from each group member anonymously, team members state the factors that affected their estimate, and the group re-estimates. Examples of this type of process include "Planning Poker" (often used with Agile Methods, see page 200) and "Wideband Delphi."

- **Strengths:** Group participation in creating the estimate increases commitment to accurate estimates as well as ownership of the final results.
- **Weaknesses:** If individual group members are biased, the negative effect can be multiplied. Groupthink (see page 181) is also a risk.
- **Keys to Success:** Consistency in how a final decision or estimate is reached will allow individual members to more actively engage in the process of creating an estimate each time this method is used.

Consensus Decision-Making

The distinction between unanimous agreement and consensus is an important one, and organizational, social, and political groups often need to reach a decision efficiently and reasonably with all parties supporting the final choice in order to be effective. For more on this, search the term "consensus decision-making."

Other Estimation Methods

At least in part, most estimation methods use one or more of the above, but some use inputs such as mathematical/statistical models (i.e. parametric estimating) or choose to focus more heavily on specific elements of a project such as risks or size rather than the time to complete the project. Many

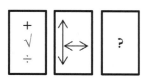

industries and domains (software, building, civil engineering, etc.) have their own methods and distinctions.

The level of detail needed to make an accurate estimate is often dictated by how far along you've progressed in the project. If this is the case, it may be prudent to change your estimation method one or more times to better suit the situation or needs you're presented with. For example, a project that doesn't yet have resources may start with a top-down approach, transitioning to group consensus once people have joined the team. This way, a project leader can consider and engage the strengths (and avoid the weaknesses) of estimation methods as a project continues.

The One-to-Two Rule

Wondering how "small" to go when dividing tasks? The "one-to-two rule" states that tasks or work units have been divided up sufficiently when the smallest ones can be completed by one or two resources in one or two weeks. At this size, individual tasks are easily understood and small enough to allow for consistent demonstrated progress.

Though estimating is important, it's vital to remember that these estimates should flow into actual schedules—estimating is simply a tool designed to help project teams properly make decisions about their future plans.

3.3 Estimates vs. Commitments

Consider the following scenario:

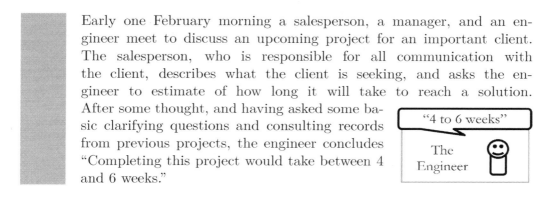

Early one February morning a salesperson, a manager, and an engineer meet to discuss an upcoming project for an important client. The salesperson, who is responsible for all communication with the client, describes what the client is seeking, and asks the engineer to estimate of how long it will take to reach a solution. After some thought, and having asked some basic clarifying questions and consulting records from previous projects, the engineer concludes "Completing this project would take between 4 and 6 weeks."

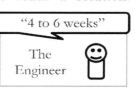

On the other hand, understanding the high priority that this particular client holds within the company, the salesperson thinks "This is such an important project and whichever resources are necessary will be available, so this project should be done as fast as possible: in 4 weeks."

Seperately, the manager, thinking about the calendar, previous experience, and given that this is the first week in February, concludes "This project should be complete between the first and third week in March."

Yet the engineer, looking at the workload currently underway, thinks "After completing the current project at the end of the month, I will have an additional 6 weeks to complete this new one."

In this scenario, each party started with the same information but ultimately ends up with wildly different perceptions about what would actually occur. As such, the person may have felt completely justified in their calculations, which may lead to future disagreements where both parties feel passionately that they are right. To put it simply, this is a problem of *estimates vs. commitments*, which can be exacerbated by the following conditions:

- The expectations of each party aren't aligned or communicated
- Assumptions are being made or data is being interpreted differently
- Individuals have different information available to them
- Some feel that open communication isn't allowed or prudent
- Individuals have biases or lack of experience that make them inherently inaccurate at estimation

Varying Perspectives

Think about the above scenario from each person's perspective. Are any of the parties more correct in their particular assertions? Do any of the negative conditions listed above seem present? Which role(s) have you played? What could have been said or done to ensure that these differences didn't occur?

Given the difficulties that estimating presents, what can be done to help the team avoid some of the pitfalls seen above? Approaching this problem requires a clear understanding of *accuracy and precision*, covered in the next section.

Expectation Management
One concept that could help immensely as the scenario above continues into execution of the project is *expectation management*. Covered in chapter 5 of this book (page 171), this communication concept focuses on ensuring that all parties have a proper understanding of important project information such as estimates and schedules.

3.4 Accuracy and Precision

Two words that are often incorrectly used interchangeably are *accuracy* and *precision*. Although related, they are distinct concepts important to the way estimates are understood and presented.

Accuracy is related to how close a stated value is to reality. A simpler way to state this is to say that accuracy measures how *true* a value is. It's important to understand that accuracy is not related to intention or perception, but rather to actual values. In a project, for instance, the time or financial estimate is measured for accuracy compared to the actual time or resources required to complete the project. Accuracy cannot truly be measured until the estimated work is completed.

Precision relates to how *exact* a stated value is. By definition, a range is less precise than a single value, and a larger range is less precise than a smaller range. Unlike accuracy, precision is related to the way a value is stated, so it's possible to state a very precise value that is not at all correct when compared to the actual value.

When these two concepts are used correctly, projects approach *consistent accuracy* and *increasing precision*. This is typically demonstrated as a smaller and smaller estimated range as the project progresses. This creates a "cone of uncertainty":[1]

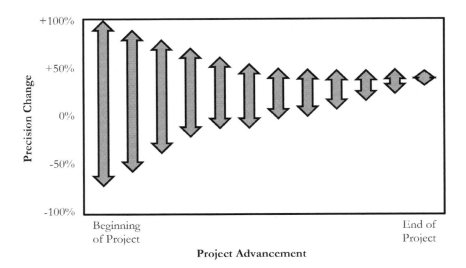

It's important to note that this concept should demonstrate a consistent level of accuracy. This means that to the best of their ability, the estimator tries to maintain truthfulness as the project progresses. In a similar graph displaying accuracy change over time, the result is much less interesting:

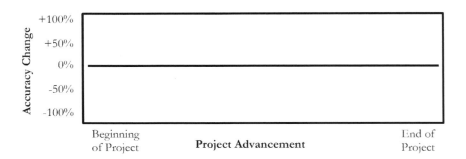

To put it plainly, to be truthful (*accurate*) early in the project, the team must admit that they're not sure about future circumstances, but believe that the outcome will fall in a range of possibility. In other words, *estimates should never be a one-time, static number*, but, rather, as the project progresses, estimates (expressed as ranges) should be revised to increase their precision (i.e. smaller and smaller ranges). The idea of a "precise estimate" is, by its very nature, an oxymoron.

Surviving in a World That Values Precision Over Accuracy

Consider this. You've been asked to estimate a project, but how can you properly account for both accuracy and precision in your estimates? One basic strategy is to decrease precision in early estimates, resulting in higher accuracy:

- **Ranges:** "6-8 Months," "400-450 person-hours"
- **Plus/minus qualifiers:** "7 Weeks +/– 1 Week"
- **Rough dates:** "2 quarters after project kickoff"

This approach includes many of the problems included in the scenario above. Because they are imprecise, more specific (precise) estimates may be requested or demanded. In this case, additional strategies may be needed:

- **Confidence factors:** "4 weeks: 30% chance, 5 weeks: 50% chance"
- **Best/worst/most likely cases:** "best case: 16 weeks, worst case: 22 weeks, most likely: 20 weeks"
- **Situational qualification:** "25 weeks; with an additional resource, reduce by 2 weeks; anticipated solution proves to be invalid, increase by 4 weeks"

In some cases other parties may have their own ideas about how long things should take or may simply cut every estimate they receive by 20%, for example. In this case, the following strategies may be required in addition to those listed above:

- Validate estimates by sharing the methods, calculations, and decision processes used to create them.
- Offer to cut scope or ask for additional resources (see *Quality and The Project Triangle* on page 43).

In the long term, the following strategies can help make acceptance of your estimates easier:

- Consistently accurate estimates bolster credibility and respect for the processes used by the team (including the estimation process).
- Consistently updating stakeholders with more and more precise estimates as the project progresses will increase confidence in your ability to manage priorities (narrowing the cone of uncertainty).

3.5   Project Scheduling

Often occurring directly after estimating, scheduling is the act of organizing, ordering, and ultimately placing the tasks and work units against real dates. In reality, scheduling's relationship to estimating is part of the *scheduling continuum*, seen to the right. Before individual dates or durations are even considered, the planning begins, outputting a list of activities, tasks, and/or work units. Estimating, covered previously, attempts to quantify the size and effort (typically in person-hours) of of project activities and tasks. Scheduling, covered in this section, seeks to add order and concrete dates to these abstract work units. Tracking, covered in the next section, attempts to ascertain how the project is progressing throughout execution.

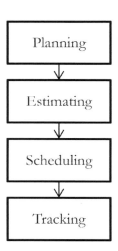

The Work Breakdown Structure

Planning and estimating efforts often yield reasonable expectations as to what is to be done and how long it will take, but it's often the case that before scheduling efforts can start, work units or activities need to be further broken down to the task level. Though there are multiple methods to do this, one of the most well-known is the *Work Breakdown Structure.*[2] Simply put, the Work Breakdown Structure (WBS) is a method of continuously breaking down elements until they are at a level that's easily understandable (and therefore can be more easily estimated and sequenced). Typically, a Work Breakdown Structure is annotated in one of two ways: as a series of nested "bullets," or as a similar graphical representation.

1. Pack
    1.1. Acquire Materials
        1.1.1. Acquire Boxes
        1.1.2. Acquire Tape
    1.2. Pack Into Boxes
        1.2.1. Pack Kitchen
            1.2.1.1. Pack Dishes
        1.2.2. Pack Bedroom
2. Move
    2.1. Find ~~Suckers~~ Friends
    2.2. Load Truck
    2.3. Drive Truck
3. Clean
    3.1. Clean Floor
        3.1.1. Sweep Floor
        3.1.2. Mop Floor

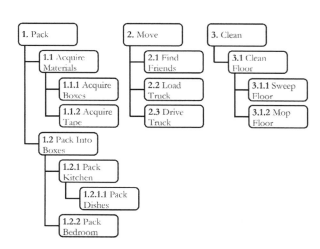

It's important to note that not all parts of a Work Breakdown Structure should be broken down to the same level; rather they only need to be broken down enough for scheduling activities to move forward (see *The One-to-Two Rule* on page 83).

Work Breakdown Structure Building Techniques

Similar to the estimating techniques covered earlier in the chapter, a Work Breakdown Structure can be built "top-down" or "bottom-up" (see page 81). However, because of its structural flexibility, it can be built "rolling wave" style or even with sticky notes on a wall. Getting the team involved in creating the structure decreases the chance of overlooking details and also promotes ownership of the project at hand.

Sequencing Tasks

Once tasks, work units, and activities have been properly broken down, it's important to sequence them properly. Remember that some tasks require others to be completed before they can be started—this is known as *precedence*. In many cases, tasks that precede others are related to each other (meaning one must be completed before another can be started), but in some cases they may simply be assigned to the same team member, not allowing them to be completed simultaneously. This sequencing is typically done using *precedence techniques*. First, estimated tasks are listed with their dependent tasks.

	Task	Estimated Duration	Dependencies
A	Move Obstacles	4 Min	Start
B	Find Broom	3 Min	Start
C	Sweep Floor	8 Min	A, B
D	Find Mop & Bucket	3 Min	Start
E	Fill Bucket with Water	2 Min	D
F	Mop Floor	15 Min	C, E

Although considered individually, each task is quite understandable; someone reading this chart, however, might have difficulty understanding things like which tasks can be completed simultaneously or how long they will take altogether. To best answer these questions, use the *Precedence Diagram Method*, seen on the next page.

After creating this diagram, it's easy to see that multiple resources can work simultaneously and that the entire "project" should take 27 minutes from start to finish:

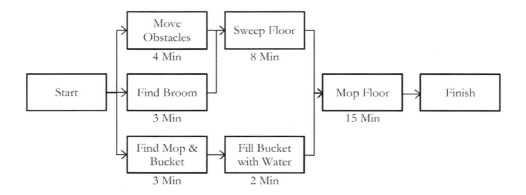

Precedence Diagram Method Terminology
The *critical path* is the longest path through the diagram, and therefore represents the total time. It also represents the tasks that, if delayed, will have the largest effect on the total project. *Slack time* refers to tasks that can be started late without affecting the schedule. In the example above, "Find Broom" has a slack time of 1 minute and is not on the critical path. Tasks on the critical path have no slack time.

Once tasks have been properly sequenced, they can be applied to a "calendarized" schedule. Project teams need to understand that even though a project is planned, estimated, and sequenced, there are many factors that can affect how the work is applied to an actual calendar. Examples include:

- Other projects or work that must be completed first
- Capital, external contractor, resource, or key personnel unavailability until a future date
- External factors such as weather and government regulation dictating when work can occur
- Organizational policies prohibiting work during certain periods such as "peak season" or holidays
- Schedule-affecting risks occurring (see *Risk Management* later in this chapter)

Additionally, plans and reality can be disparate, so *tracking*, covered later in this chapter, becomes a vital activity for successful project teams.

Visualizing the Schedule

Though scheduling decisions are relatively straightforward, visualizing them can be a challenge. Individual projects often exist in organizations that have a lot going on—

other projects, operational work, multiple departments, and distant stakeholders. Cutting through this noise requires simple, easily updated visualizations created by the project leader and viewed by the project team and other stakeholders.

One common way of marking time in a project is through *milestones*. A milestone is an accomplishment that in itself isn't any work and doesn't appear in the sequence of tasks, but represents a point in time. Most often, a milestone is simply the beginning or end of a phase. Examples could include "building begins" or "testing complete" milestones. By calculating milestone dates and organizing these into a chart, an easy-to-understand, high-level view of the project schedule can be shared:

ID	Milestone	Planned(+/− 1 Week)	Actual
01	Design Begins	May 12	
02	Design Complete	June 15	
03	Module 1 Construction Begins	June 18	
04	Module 2 Construction Begins	June 22	
05	Construction Complete	July 14	
06	Delivery to Customer Complete	July 18	

It's important to note that this chart should include both the planned date and an empty column to allow actual dates to be recorded as the project proceeds—this allows any anticipated lack of precision to be expressed as the visualization is used.

Another commonly used schedule visualization tool is a *Gantt chart*. Though individual features may vary (labeling, hierarchy, precedence, columns), all Gantt charts have tasks or activities listed on the vertical axis and bars indicating length of time corresponding to the horizontal axis. By viewing how bars are "stacked," the project team can determine which tasks are scheduled to happen before or concurrent to others.

ID	Name	Duration	May 1 – May 7	May 8 – May 15	May 16 – May 22
1	Main Part				
2	- Task A	2 Days			
3	- Task B	1 Day			
4	- Task C	8 Days			
5	- Task D	2 Days			
6	Module 1				
7	- Task E	6 Days			
8	- Task F	7 Days			
9	Complete	Milestone			

In most cases, modern project teams use server-based project systems. Built to assist in planning, estimating, scheduling, and tracking, these systems hold large amounts of information designed to aid in the visualization and manipulation of project data. Often each team member has access to a slightly different view: some, for example, may only have permission to view their own tasks, while project leaders are usually able to view and manage the project in its entirety.

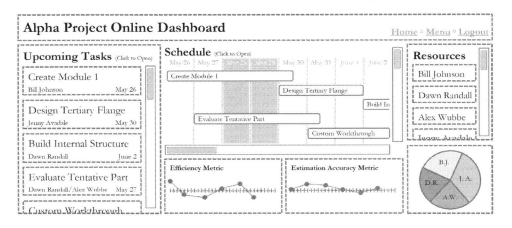

Note that the illustration above is an example and does not represent an actual project management application. These systems often include multiple layers of data and visualizations such as:

- Activities or tasks, including visualizations like Gantt charts
- Project calendars and milestones
- Listings of current issues and risks
- Information about stakeholders connected to the project (see *Stakeholders* on page 12)
- Project artifact (documentation) file listings
- Financial information relating to the project such as budgets and materials available
- Statistics relating to the project (see *Communicating with Metrics and Reports* on page 164)

Though immensely helpful, these systems often have a relatively steep learning curve and require conscientious effort. Users need to input changes that have occurred, tasks that have been completed, the status of stakeholders, budget information, and much more. What's more, if the system's data is even slightly out of date, its usefulness significantly declines. Because of this, it's likely that a significant portion of a project leader's time will be spent in these endeavors. Though this may seem to be a recent phenomenon, the reality is that projects have always required significant effort devoted to record keeping—modern systems have made this more efficient, consistent, and share-able. (One can only imagine how long it would take to update a Gantt chart manually, and thankfully, those times are behind us.)

Paralyzed by Too Much Data?

Better visualizing available project information can lead to more efficient decision making—but can it backfire? Because so much data exists and there is always the potential for collecting more, some decision makers may become paralyzed. As they look for a definitive answer in the "numbers," they may become concerned that they don't have all of the necessary information to carry out the project, or may simply be overwhelmed with large amounts of data or the systems used to collect and analyze them. It's important to remember that advancing the project schedule is as important during the early planning stages as it is later on, and a balance must be struck between analysis and advancement (for a related pitfall, see *Analysis Paralysis* on page 184).

Communication of Schedule Elements

Just because the tools and visualizations above are useful to you as a project leader or team member, doesn't mean they're appropriate for stakeholders. Considering elements such as level of detail and how information may be interpreted requires careful evaluation of who you're communicating with as well as what is to be communicated. Several sections of chapter 5 address this directly: see *Communicating with Metrics and Reports* on page 164 and *Stakeholder Expectation Management* on page 171.

Scheduling and Process

Now that you've gained a basic understanding of how to break down work, sequence tasks, and visualize the schedule, it's time to step back and consider the context surrounding how work is done by your team. Discussed in chapter 2 (see *Values, Needs, and Process* on page 36), the process your team has chosen to adopt significantly influences how the work is carried out. Examples include:

- How work is divided among resources

- Whether planning and work can be conducted simultaneously
- How often to check in with the customer and management
- The amount of testing or verification that must be conducted for each task
- "Ownership" of work - is it individual(s), or the entire team?
- How much the team is willing to adapt to changes

Following the guidelines of established process, the project team is now able to create a schedule that works within the constraints of the project and the culture of their organization. The makeup of that schedule is as variable as projects themselves, but one truth applies to all schedules: unless the executed work is tracked and the schedule adjusted to changing conditions, the planning, estimating, and scheduling effort expended thus far goes largely to waste.

3.6   Project Tracking

After a project has been planned, estimated, and scheduled, the work begins. At this point, many teams choose to concentrate solely on this work, only stopping occasionally to look around, roughly ascertain where they are, and return to work. In reality, even the most diligent project leaders can only view the status of a project in intervals. In the illustration below, project *visibility* is only achieved in the gaps, which typically happen when project phases change or work is handed off from one party to another:[3]

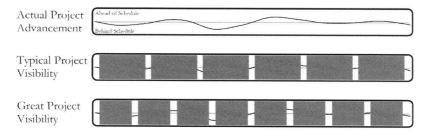

Given how little visibility a team may have into the project progress, it's difficult to see how the leader can gain more insight into the status of the project's activities. *Project tracking* involves two basic steps.

1. When estimating and scheduling, ensure that project tasks have an appropriate level of *granularity*. In other words, try to optimize the size of work units for track-ability (see *The One-to-Two Rule* on page 83).

2. Assign each task or work unit an appropriately (and relatively) sized *Earned Value.*

What exactly is Earned Value? Imagine a project with the following status:

Work Unit	Completion Status
Conceptual Design	Complete
Detailed Specification	Complete
Build	In Progress
Documentation	In Progress
User Manual Production	Not Started
Testing	Not Started

How complete is this project? 40%? 50%? 60%? Based on the data, it's nearly impossible to tell, and trying to answer the question only brings new ones to light. How complete is the "Build" work unit? Does it take a lot more resources or time than "User Manual Production"? Now imagine the same project with more information.

Work Unit	Completion Status
Conceptual Design	200/200
Detailed Specification	300/300
Build	150/600
Documentation	10/100
User Manual Production	0/400
Testing	0/500

With this new information, the *Earned Value* of each work unit, we can precisely calculate our level of completion: $660 / 2100 \times 100 = 31\%$ complete. Earned Value provides a uniform measure for project progress for the entire project or any sub-element and is easily compared to other measures such as percentage of resources expended or percentage of scheduled time incurred. In the above example, if one half of our budgeted time has elapsed, it becomes obvious that the project is behind schedule.

What About Partial Credit?

The above example looks at work units (i.e. groups of tasks), such as "Detailed Specification," but what about individual tasks? Typically, at the individual task level, the entire Earned Value credit is only issued when the task is 100% complete. This eliminates perpetually "95% done" tasks and highlights the importance of an appropriate level of task *granularity.*

Visualizing Project Tracking

It's time to revisit the visualization tools discussed in the scheduling section; these become even more useful during tracking. The milestone chart, for instance, can be updated to include actual dates while also keeping a consistent format previously seen by stakeholders. Note that the planned dates are changed as actual milestone dates are recorded:

ID	Milestone	Planned	Actual
01	Design Begins	May 12 ✓	May 12
02	Design Complete	June 15 ✓	June 15
03	Module 1 Construction Begins	June 18 ✓	June 18
04	Module 2 Construction Begins	June 22 X	June 24
05	Construction Complete	~~July 14~~ July 17	
06	Delivery to Customer Complete	~~July 18~~ July 21	

Gantt charts can also be updated to include tracking information. By including "percent complete" data (on the bars) and drawing a vertical line to indicate the current date, it becomes apparent whether the project is on track or behind schedule.

ID	Name	Duration	%			
1	Main Part				Now	
2	- Task A	2 Days	100%			
3	- Task B	1 Day	100%			
4	- Task C	8 Days	50%			
5	- Task D	2 Days	100%			
6	Module 1					
7	- Task E	6 Days	75%			
8	- Task F	7 Days	0%			
9	Complete	Milestone				

Server-based tools are typically well-balanced to include both scheduling and tracking functionality and often allow users to view multiple types of reports and visualizations (look again at the example on page 92).

Beyond Tracking

So what happens after tracking? Because projects rarely go exactly as planned, the process of tracking often reveals new information, unplanned delays, inaccuracies in estimating, and unrealistic schedules that you need to address throughout the project. The answer to what happens after tracking is the same as what happens before tracking—planning, estimating, scheduling, and more tracking. These four activities are cyclical in nature, meaning that tracking curves back to planning. Even if changes in the schedule aren't needed, the section on *Accuracy and Precision* (page 85) tells us that as the project advances, more information will become available and we can be increasingly precise in our estimates and schedules.

But can anything be done about these problems before scheduling and tracking? The next section reveals a few possibilities.

3.7   Risk Management

> ***Risks are problems that haven't happened yet.***

Risks, especially schedule-related risks, are an important part of creating and quantifying a plan and schedule. But what makes something a risk rather than a fact or circumstance? Risks are characterized by the following:

- **Uncertainty:** A probability greater than 0% and less than 100%. Risks with a probability of 100% are called facts, and are not uncertain. Considering scenarios with a 0% chance of occurring is a waste of energy.

- **An associated loss:** This can include money, reputation, time, etc., but most projects focus on risks that would primarily impact the schedule.

- **Manageability:** This means that a team could, within reason, do something to affect its impact or the probability of it occurring. An asteroid crashing into earth is not within the manageable scope of most projects, so it should not be given attention.

Everyone is aware of risks, and some even choose to point them out, but a responsible project team takes the time to *identify, analyze,* and *respond to* risks. In this case, the team is choosing to be proactive rather than reactive.

Risk Identification

How can you identify risks? The act of finding and recording risks is itself a separate process and should be considered with this in mind.[4] Executed properly, an entire team and any key stakeholders in a project are consulted and actively participate in the identification of risks. This can be done in a series of independent meetings, or as a portion of a regular meeting that occurs throughout the project.

Possibly the most important feature of risk identification is its perpetual nature—the project team should be seeking and identifying risks throughout the entire project, not just at its inception. Risks can come from many different areas:

- **Stakeholders:** Are there areas where stakeholder-specified requirements seem likely to change? What if you missed a major stakeholder?

- **The project team:** What if key team members aren't available during vital phases? What if you can't find the right people?

- **Technology:** Would a machine breakdown halt the project? Are servers properly backed up?

- **The organization:** Are there other projects competing for your resources? Do some steps require direct intervention by management?

- **Finances:** Is the project fully funded? What if some equipment costs more than anticipated?

- **Competition:** Could a competitor releasing a new product change the viability of the product? What would happen if a competitor gained knowledge of your project's details?

- **Law/contracts:** Do government regulations require approval that may delay your progress? Does the contract allow customers to change the delivery date?

- **Environmental:** Would a weather event delay the project? Would a political event make offshore resources unavailable?

SWOT Analysis

A useful tool that aids in the discovery of risks is SWOT analysis, which uses a basic grid as follows:

	Positive	Negative
Internal	Strengths	**Weaknesses**
External	Opportunities	**Threats**

Together, a team examines the project for internal **S**trengths and **W**eaknesses and external **O**pportunities and **T**hreats. *Weaknesses* and *threats* are often risks to the project.

SWOT Your Project
Think about a project that you are currently leading or participating in. What are some of the internal strengths and weaknesses? Are they related to personnel? Process? What about any external opportunities and threats? Are they related to other organizations? Market conditions?

Remember that risks need to be sufficiently narrow to be specifically identifiable. Broad, generic risks such as "Loss of personnel" aren't specific enough to help you reasonably ascertain how they may negatively affect a project. A better, more specific example could be "Loss of testing resource in phase 3." Once identified, risks are recorded in a *risk register*:

ID	Risk				
1	Team is unable to acquire proper license before phase 2				
2	Resources not released from the Jenson Project on time				
3					

Risk Analysis

Because the degree to which a risk can impact a project's schedule (or cost and quality) varies, the project team must quantify the impact of any risks as they proceed. This is done by estimating the probability of the risk occurring, the impact (typically in hours, days, or weeks) that the occurrence of the risk would have on the project, and multiplying the two together. This calculates the *Risk Exposure*.

$$\textit{Risk Exposure} = \textit{Probability} \times \textit{Impact}$$

Although quantifying these two values can be difficult and may seem subjective, it's imperative to project success. Using some of the estimating techniques discussed earlier in this chapter (see *Estimation Methods* on page 80) and frequently reevaluating the values as the project progresses (see *Accuracy and Precision* on page 85) are key factors in helping the team achieve more accurate results. It can be helpful (and more accurate) to express probability and impact as "chunkier" units, i.e. 10% / 20% / 1 week rather then 14.6% / 5.3 days, refining them as more information becomes available.

These calculated values are added to the risk register. Once this is complete, risks are reordered by calculated Risk Exposure, with the highest priority (the risks that need to be monitored most diligently) at the top of the list.

ID	Risk	Probability	Impact	R.E.	
2	Resources not released from the Jenson Project on time	30%	1.5 Weeks	0.45 Weeks	
1	Team is unable to acquire proper license before phase 2	20%	2 Weeks	0.4 Weeks	
3					

Risk Response

While being aware of risks that threaten a project is helpful, the ultimate benefit appears when these risks are pacified, or *mitigated*. In many cases, organizations wait until a crisis has occurred or a failure has been detected to address them—a reactive approach. A more proactive project team employs risk mitigation strategies *before* the risk has occurred to reduce the probability of it occurring or the impact it will have on a project. Common strategies include:

- **Avoidance:** Removing the risky part of the project, for example. In the case of a severe risk, canceling the project altogether may be prudent.

- **Knowledge acquisition:** Common examples include research or prototyping a product for a customer before proceeding.

- **Transference:** Two strategies include assigning a part of the project to a team better equipped to handle the risk or moving the risky tasks off the schedule's critical path (see *Precedence Diagram Method Terminology* on page 90).

The last option is often used when the strategies above are unavailable or carrying them out would cost more than the risk itself:

- **Acceptance:** In this case, a management plan is formulated in case the risk occurs. This plan helps you accept the risk while also working to mitigate its overall effects on a project.

When risks must remain a part of the project, you must record their planned mitigation or management strategy in the risk register. Stakeholders are generally much more comfortable knowing that the team has identified, analyzed, and responded to a risk rather than facing a problem that suddenly appears from seemingly nowhere.

ID	Risk	Probability	Impact	R.E.	Mitigation(s)/ Management
2	Resources not released from the Jenson Project on time	30%	1.5 Weeks	0.45 Weeks	Move impacted tasks later in project
1	Team is unable to acquire proper license before phase 2	20%	2 Weeks	0.4 Weeks	Outsource server to ServCo until launch
3					

Ultimately the Total Risk Exposure should be accounted for in the project schedule. Although it may be tempting to attach risks individually to work units or activities (which increases their estimated durations), they're better added to the project as a single unit. In reality, some risks will occur and some won't; project managers rely on the aggregation of risk, meaning that in the end those that occur and those that don't occur are likely to balance each other out. Instead of "padding the schedule," a calculated, justifiable number is available (the Total Risk Exposure) to add to the final schedule (and/or budget).

The Opposite of Risks
This section explains the strategies behind managing risks (weaknesses and threats), but what about the other 2 letters in SWOT, *Strengths* and *Opportunities*? In the same way that a team can avoid or mitigate risks, they can attempt to exploit, enhance, or share opportunities. The strategies are opposite of risk management, but the application is similar.

Risks Within Your Project
Using a spreadsheet or word processor, record some of the risks that may impact a project you're currently leading or are a part of. If your colleagues are available, work separately to create individual lists, and then collaborate to estimate the probability and impact of the risks all of you identified.

ID	Risk	Probability	Impact	R.E.	Mitigation(s) /Management

Whether we like it or not, the people, or stakeholders, associated with any project typically represent the largest share of risk. Understanding their potential for disruption is an important part of risk management; finding, categorizing, and prioritizing stakeholders is covered in the next section.

3.8 Chapter Tool: Prioritizing Stakeholders

Now that we've gained a solid understanding of the prioritization of tasks and risks, we can now address stakeholders: how to find them, what effects they can have on the project, and how they're affected by the project.

When it comes to finding stakeholders, the following guidelines are important to remember:

- **Finding stakeholders is a team effort:** Like risk identification, a more complete list requires everyone's participation. Brainstorming can be an effective tool here.

- **Start early and revisit often:** The team should use early project activities such as feasibility studies and requirements gathering to search for stakeholders. As the project progresses, stakeholder identification should be revisited often.

- **Stakeholders can be groups:** One common mistake is to try and identify every individual stakeholder by name. If groups of people have a similar relationship to the project, identify and manage them as a group until circumstances require a change.

- **Keep a record of stakeholders:** A typical format for this is the *stakeholder register*.

Stakeholder Register

The *stakeholder register* is simply a table containing information about a project's stakeholders. The following is an example of what a basic wedding stakeholder register may look like:

ID	Name	Title	Info	Notes
1	Erin	Bride	Local	
2	Brian	Groom	Local	

ID	Name	Title	Info	Notes
3	Julia	Mother of the Bride	Santa Clara, CA	Visiting 3 weeks before
4		Parents of Bride & Groom	Orlando, FL	
5	Maria	Maid of Honor	Local	
6	Phil	Best Man	Local	
7		Wedding Party		
8	Delicioso Catering Co.	Caterer	555-1234	
9	Rev. Smith	Officiant	555-5678	
10	Uncle Joe	Guests		Likes parties
11	Bride/Groom's Family	Guests	RSVP List	
12		Guests	RSVP List	

Note that this list would generally be under constant revision, with new stakeholders and details being added regularly. Now that we've created a list of stakeholders, we can start analyzing what their needs are and how they relate to the project. Generally, stakeholders will fall into one of four classifications:[5]

- **Manage closely:** These stakeholders are the most important. They need to be fully engaged and will require the greatest efforts on your part.

- **Keep satisfied:** Also high in importance, these stakeholders need to be engaged because of the dramatic effect that they can have on the project.

- **Keep informed:** These stakeholders care about the project's outcome but do not represent as much risk to the project.

- **Monitor:** Although they currently represent little risk, it's important to monitor these stakeholders in case their role, interest, or risk level changes.

Determining which of these strategy groups a stakeholder belongs to requires us to remember the definition of a stakeholder originally stated on page 12:

> ***Stakeholders are people who can affect or are affected by the execution or outcome of a project.***

"Can affect" implies stakeholder's *power* over the project. "Are affected by" implies stakeholder's *interest* in the project. Expressed as a chart, these look like this:

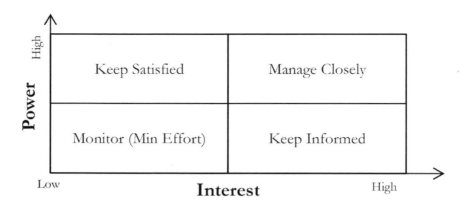

Rating each project stakeholder's power and interest in a project becomes an important step in deciding how to effectively engage them, affecting communication most of all (*Stakeholder Expectation Management* is a topic of chapter 5 on page 171). Given this new information, the stakeholder register can be updated with several more columns:

ID	Name	Title	Info	Notes	Power	Interest	Strategy
1	Erin	Bride	Local				
2	Brian	Groom	Local				
3	Julia	Mother of the Bride	Santa Clara, CA	Visiting 3 weeks before			
4		Parents of Bride & Groom	Orlando, FL				
5	Maria	Maid of Honor	Local				
6	Phil	Best Man	Local				
7		Wedding Party					
8	Delicioso Catering Co.	Caterer	555-1234				
9	Rev. Smith	Officiant	555-5678				
10	Uncle Joe	Guests		Likes parties			
11	Bride/-Groom's Family	Guests	RSVP List				
12		Guests	RSVP List				

What About Uncle Joe?

Uncle Joe is like any other wedding guest, right? Low power, low interest—monitoring is all that's needed here—but what if that changes? Monitoring is important because if the stakeholder's power or interest changes, strategies must also change. Uncle Joe doesn't know his limits, and when this happens, the situation switches from "monitor" to "manage closely."

Like the risk register, the stakeholder register needs to be updated as time passes, new information becomes available, and circumstances change. In some cases, it's possible to know how a stakeholder's power and interest is likely to change. For example, as the time a vital component is needed approaches in the project timeline, the opportunity to seek alternate suppliers diminishes, and the stakeholder (supplier) management strategy changes.

Power, Interest, and Strategy

For each row in the table on the previous page, evaluate each stakeholder by their level of power and interest on a scale of low, medium, high, and very high. After writing down each number and their power/interest level, determine the appropriate strategy by examining the power/interest grid above and record that as well. Create some new rows, add new stakeholders, and evaluate them according to each column as well.

Your Stakeholders

Think about a project you're currently undertaking. In a table similar to the one below, fill in the major stakeholder groups as well as any relevant information for each. Evaluate their level of power and interest and finally an appropriate strategy for each. Remember that stakeholders also include your team and management (and obviously the customer).

ID	Name	Title	Info	Notes	Power	Interest	Strategy

3.9   Summary and Conclusion

At its very core, project leadership is about prioritization. In most cases, this means deciding that one action or work unit should precede another. This can also mean choosing not to add certain aspects to a project because of the time or budget available. To a proactive project team, this means accounting for what risks could occur and choosing what actions are needed there as well. By analyzing stakeholder power and interest, prioritizing effort can be determined for stakeholder engagement and communication.

Ultimately, it's important to remember that these prioritizations represent actions, deliverables, and projects that are important to people—the stakeholders who affect or are affected by the project. Because of this, a project leader also needs to prioritize the interpersonal relationships within in the project, prioritizing cooperation over dictation, collaboration over negotiation, all while equating honest, accurate communication with professionalism.

In the next two chapters, we'll discuss team dynamics and communicating effectively, both vital to the concepts discussed above. Our goal remains to integrate what you've just learned with your growing knowledge of project and team management.

Key Terms

Accuracy: How close a stated value is to reality; its level of *truth*. Should not be confused with *precision* (page 85).

Critical Path: Within a project schedule, the sequence of tasks that (if changed) will affect the expected project completion time. These tasks have no *slack time* (page 90).

Earned Value: The actual amount of work completed on a project. Often expressed as a percentage and compared against the actual resources and time used so far (page 95).

Estimation: The process of assessing the time and cost expected for project phases, tasks, work units, or *risks*. Often used as the basis for *scheduling* (page 80).

Expert Judgement: A determination made by one or more individuals based on experience, knowledge, or analysis. Typically used for *estimation* (page 80).

Gantt Chart: A visual representation of the project's schedule. Typically the horizontal axis includes a timescale with horizontal bars representing task lengths (page 91, 96).

Granularity: The scale or level of detail which something possesses. Typically applied to the breakdown of tasks or activities (page 94).

Milestone: A project accomplishment that represents a significant point in time. Often marks the beginning or end of a phase (page 91).

One-to-Two Rule: Tasks or work units have been divided up sufficiently when they can be completed by one or two resources in one to two weeks (page 83).

Precedence: When sequencing tasks or activities, the indication that one task or activity must come before or is more important than another (page 89).

Precision: How exact a stated value is, whether *accurate* or otherwise (page 85).

Project Visibility: The ability of stakeholders to ascertain project status, especially as it relates to *scheduling* (page 94).

Risk: A project-affecting problem that hasn't yet happened. Characterized by uncertainty, some degree of manageability, and an expected loss (page 97).

Risk Exposure: The probability of a *risk* occurring multiplied by its impact on the project, typically resulting in an estimated schedule or financial impact (page 99).

Risk Register: A list of project *risks* and information about them. Risks with highest *Risk Exposure* are placed on the top of the list (page 99).

Scheduling: The act of organizing, ordering, and ultimately placing project phases, tasks, and work units against real dates. Typically used as a basis for *tracking* (page 88).

Slack Time: Within a project schedule, the tasks that can be delayed without affecting the expected project completion time. These tasks are not part of the *critical path*. Also known as *float* (page 90).

Stakeholder Register: A table containing information about a project's stakeholders. Typically contains contact information and their power/interest profile (page 102).

Tracking: The act of gaining insight into the status of the project's activities, especially those previously *scheduled* (page 94).

Review Questions

1. A team has chosen to find a similar project in order to draw conclusions about how long their current project will take. Which estimation method have they selected?

2. You're trying to estimate the total length of a project, but the individual components and activities aren't yet known and seem likely to change. Which estimation method is least useful?

3. You are trying to complete a top-down estimation. According to the one-to-two rule, at what point have you reached enough granularity?

4. "A measure of how exact a value is." Is this accuracy or precision?

5. Using the project information below, what is the current earned value?

Task	Status
Planning	150/150
Section 1 Build	320/500
Section 2 Build	150/600
Completion	0/100

6. Risk ID 4 has been on the list for 3 weeks now. It has a probability of 20% and a 5 week impact. What is its Risk Exposure?

7. It is determined that a project stakeholder has low interest and high power. What management strategy should be used?

Exercises

1. You have given the general manager of your organization an estimate of 4-6 weeks for the next phase of the project, but you're worried that she will assume the 4 weeks instead of the range. How would you address this?

2. As a project progresses, estimates relating to the expected completion date should become more precise while keeping a consistent level of accuracy. What are the dangers of overly precise estimates early in the project?

3. A major stakeholder is adamant that your estimate be an exact number, stating that the previous project leader had always delivered very precise estimates. What strategies can you use here?

4. Identify the components of a basic home and organize them into a work breakdown structure at least 3 levels deep (example: Bedroom→Bed→Pillow, Blanket).

5. You're considering whether to share a milestone chart or a Gantt chart with an executive who is interested in your project. Give two advantages and two disadvantages of using each type of schedule visualization.

6. Using the tasks below, create a precedence diagram, determine the duration needed to complete the tasks, and label the critical path.

	Task	Estimated Duration	Dependencies
A	Confirm # of Attendees	5 Min	Start
B	Print Name Tags	30 Min	A
C	Set Up Tables	30 Min	A
D	Confirm Catering	10 Min	A
E	Place Table Linens	20 Min	C
F	Place Name Tags	10 Min	B, E

7. A project leader currently tracks work progress by asking each team member what their status is each week. What are three things that they could do to increase project visibility?

8. Your department has decided to change office locations and you've been placed in charge of planning the move. List 5 different risks and formulate mitigation or management responses for each.

9. Using the columns below, list 5 stakeholders or stakeholder groups for a pizza delivery business. Be sure to analyze each stakeholder's level of power and interest.

ID	Name	Title	Info	Notes	Power	Interest	Strategy

Notes

[1] McConnell, Steve. *Software Project Survival Guide: how to be sure your first important project isn't your last.* Redmond, WA: Microsoft Press. p. 31. 1998.

[2] Project Management Institute. *A Guide to the Project Management Body of Knowledge – Fifth Edition.* Project Management Institute Inc. p. 125-132. 2013.

[3] McConnell, Steve. *Rapid Development: Taming Wild Software Schedules.* Redmond, WA: Microsoft Press. p. 57. 1996.

[4] Project Management Institute. *A Guide to the Project Management Body of Knowledge – Fifth Edition.* Project Management Institute Inc. p. 309. 2013.

[5] Project Management Institute. *A Guide to the Project Management Body of Knowledge – Fifth Edition.* Project Management Institute Inc. p. 395-397. 2013.

Team Structure and Development

In this chapter, we'll try to understand what a team is and what makes it successful. By exploring success factors, structures, stages of development, and the core needs of a team, we'll gain the ability to properly use the tools that help a team produce consistent, positive results.

When you think of a team, what comes to mind? Your favorite sports team? A team at work? What about a team you may be on? If you're thinking of a healthy team, you're probably thinking of a group of people whose structure shares several features that healthy teams have in common: interdependence, accountability, and a common goal.

In striving to build a strong team, it's important to understand what elements help define success, how a team develops and grows, and what its needs are to remain healthy. By carefully considering who should be on the team, the type of team to build, and the environment that it will operate in, you can exponentially increase the chance of a successful project.

4.1   What Makes a Team Successful?

Other than its natural growth and progression, what makes a team successful? What are the common factors successful teams share? Is it possible for leaders to "inject" these success factors into a team? The following list includes many of the "ingredients" of a successful team:

Complimentary Skillsets

In some cases, crafting the perfect team involves considering what each member can do, which ensures that each anticipated task or objective is appropriately covered by one or more members of a team.

- **Examples:** Many small business teams, comic-book superhero teams
- **Keys to Success:** Here, a team's diversity is important, but not random or haphazard. Differences also have the potential to create incompatible teams. Additionally, if the team has come to rely on one member's unique skills, the loss of that team member can be devastating.

Common Purpose and Goals

Sometimes what attracts members to a team is that they really believe in what the team is trying to achieve. A common goal allows team members to focus on results rather than individual differences or the day-to-day.

- **Examples:** The Manhattan Project, volunteer-based charitable organizations
- **Keys to Success:** At times, the level of intensity of this type of team can disrupt other projects, and the shifting priorities of individual team members can decrease productivity.

Good Planning

Akin to an assembly line, in this team, every member knows what they need to do ahead of time, why it's important, when it needs to be completed, and whom to hand the next step off to.

- **Examples:** Auto racing pit-stop crew, "The A-Team"
- **Keys to Success:** Reliability is paramount for this type of team. Because each member's plan relies on the other's, a culture of accountability (discussed later in this chapter) is central to the team's success.

Effective Leadership

In many ways, this exemplifies what many see as the classic team structure. The formation, motivation, and substantiation of the team revolve around one or more strong, dedicated leaders.

- **Examples:** Successful sports teams, military units
- **Keys to Success:** A strong leader and team members who are willing to follow that lead mean that the leader's motivations and methods need to match the culture of the organization. Strong leadership can sometimes stifle

the individualistic nature of creativity.

Appropriate Motivators

By zeroing in on what factors motivate its employees, an organization or leader can create an environment where team members are passionate and self-motivated, taking ownership of the project and its results.

- **Examples:** Successful Silicon Valley companies, award-winning employers
- **Keys to Success:** It's important to remember that what motivates you may not be the same as what motivates other team members. Example motivators include compensation, recognition, interpersonal relationships, and interesting work (see *Motivators* on page 7).

"Chemistry"

Sometimes what makes a team work well together is hard to nail down. It may be luck, timing, personality, or destiny, but some teams are great "just because."

- **Examples:** Performance duos such as Penn & Teller, late-night talk shows
- **Keys to Success:** If you encounter a team like this, consider bringing them together again on future projects. Remember that other teams and resources exist—make sure their needs are being met to develop future team members.

Though the temptation may be to add as many of these "ingredients" as possible, a responsible team leader considers not only which elements are practical, but also the personalities and skillsets of the individuals, the culture of the organization (see *Matching Leadership with Culture* on page 10), and the type of team they're trying to build. Though there are literally hundreds of types of teams, three main categories include:[1]

- **Problem-Resolution Teams:** This type of team is fueled by the difficulty of the problem. (Success Factors: Complimentary Skillsets, Common Purpose and Goals)

- **Creativity Teams:** Tasked with creating new ideas and solutions, this team loves the unknown. (Success Factors: Appropriate Motivators, "Chemistry")

- **Tactical-Execution Teams:** Focused on creating and implementing a plan, this type of team prefers well-defined roles. (Success Factors: Good Planning, Strong Leadership)

Larson and LaFasto on Teamwork

In their book *Teamwork: What Must Go Right/What Can Go Wrong*, Larson and LaFasto define the three types of teams described above. Additionally, they describe some of the essential properties of a successful team, such as external support, competent team members, and standards of excellence. Many of these properties are described in the "ingredients" list starting on page 111 and the *Needs and the Team* section on page 124 below.

Knowing what drives a team is essential to knowing whether a proposed project team has the potential to succeed or if adjustments need to be made, but truly understanding a team involves taking a deeper look. In the next few sections, we'll cover team structure, development, needs, and even a tool designed to help evaluate the maturity of a team.

4.2   Team Structure

Before looking at the project or operational work they need to perform, a team must consider its own structure. This means looking at how the team is led and organized, the things that influence how the team is built, and the common roles that comprise it.

Though there are many variations on how a team can be organized, there are four structures that seem to be the most common: top-down, interdisciplinary, superstar-support, and large/variable-structure teams.

Top-Down Teams

This type of team structure is what many would consider the "classic" way of doing things. One person takes responsibility for the project and assigns tasks and duties to team members as they deem appropriate. The team's attachment is to the "boss."

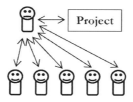

Though it may seem like this team structure would almost always use an authoritarian type of leadership style, quite the opposite is true—the leader can successfully use a combination of styles (see *Leadership Styles* on page 2). The most defining feature of this structure is the arrangement of accountability—the leader is accountable to the project and the team members are accountable to the leader. Because of their large stake of accountability, a project leader may choose this style for a number of reasons: an inexperienced team, an extremely tight deadline, or organizational/external pressures (for an example of this see *Fire Drill* on page 185).

Though top-down is a common structure, the project leader can act as a "single point of failure" if they become unavailable and there isn't anyone else equipped to take over effectively. A related problem has to do with decision making—the nature of this structure means that the people who are actually performing a project's tasks can be underrepresented when it comes to decisions.

"Top-Down?"
Does the term "top-down" sound familiar? In addition to a type of team structure, it's also an estimation method. See *Top-Down Estimation* on page 81.

Interdisciplinary Teams

Interdisciplinary teams have members who bring a variety of skills or expertise to a project. Team members' primary focus is on the project, and in many cases the project is defined with these particular individuals in mind.

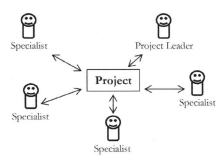

In contrast to top-down, interdisciplinary teams are often characterized by the equality of members' standing. Because teams are likely to include specialties from several different areas, it's just as likely that members will hold different ranks within the organization, earn different pay, and in some cases, include members who don't work for the same company. The varied specialties of each team member are essential to the success of the team, and members should recognize each contribution made while also treating each other as equals—even the project leader (or project manager) shouldn't be elevated—their management and communication skills are seen as essential to the project in a similar way to another member's technical expertise.

The most important element of a successful interdisciplinary team is mutual respect. Because the members of the team are often accomplished professionals, it can be easy for some to devalue the contributions of others due to the inevitable overlap in skills that may be present. As an example, a team member who's primarily responsible for customer communication may feel that the project leader's task management efforts are deficient, but if this team member took over task management, there's a good chance that customer communication would suffer.

A common pitfall for interdisciplinary teams is deadlock. When team members reach opposing conclusions, the decisions needed to move forward with the project can be difficult. Individuals may passionately believe their option is best, and even have the professional experience to back it up. Strategies for dealing with this type of issue are discussed later in the chapter (see *Managing Conflict* on page 126).

"Agile" Teams
Discussed in the appendix (*Agile: The Future of Projects?*), Agile projects are most likely to utilize interdisciplinary teams. Agile's focus on individual skills and mutual respect closely resemble the ideals of a healthy interdisciplinary team.

Superstar-Support Teams
In some cases, a single team member may be uniquely skilled, trained, or for some reason, the only one who can perform a significant part of the project work. In other cases, tasks are best performed by a single team member, with others facilitating their success. In many ways, a superstar-support team resembles a surgical team, with one individual performing the project work and others providing support by performing related tasks, setting up work environments or tools, or "jumping in" so that the superstar can perform essential tasks elsewhere. The majority of the team's focus is on the superstar, whose primary focus is on the project.

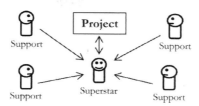

The health of this type of team hinges on a proper perspective shared among all team members. Though their focus may seem to be directed on the superstar, the real objective is the project work. Supporting team members are not subservient; rather they understand that assisting the superstar is the most efficient way of completing project objectives. The superstar also needs to focus on the project rather than themselves, treating supporting team members with professional respect and acknowledging their importance in the success of the project.

Large and Variable-Structure Teams

In some cases, the idea of a "team" can be hard to define. Is an employee of a big-box retailer a part of a team even though there could be an employee working another shift whom they've never met? What if they're a small element of a bigger project? Are the team members of that small team also team members with other small teams in the larger product effort?

In addition to being quite large, the structure of the team can be quite dynamic—you may spend a month working side-by-side with another team member only to hardly ever see them after the work unit is complete. More fluid structures often are needed for larger projects, especially when the scope includes many different types of tasks.

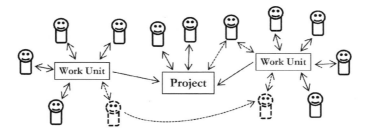

So is everyone on the same team? A simple way to address this is to think of people with whom you don't interact on a day-to-day basis less as fellow team members, and more as *stakeholders*. With the understanding that everyone associated with a product or project is, in fact, a stakeholder, we can begin to think about how our stake in the project has similarities and differences with others and how our actions are likely to affect or be affected by them (this concept is covered more comprehensively in chapter 3 on page 102).

The problems associated with large and variable-structure teams mostly have to do with organization and prioritization. Because of the complexity of both the work and the resources, project leaders have an even bigger responsibility to carefully examine and manage both the workload and the team—sometimes they will need to delegate leadership duties and create sub-teams. Because of the size or changing nature of these teams, inefficiency can be a consistent problem. Adding team members or constantly shifting team structure in response to project needs may carry diminishing returns—less impact starts to be associated with the addition of each new team member, and each time a person is moved, it takes time for that individual to reach full efficiency.

Large-Team Meetings

Have you ever been in a meeting that seemed to have so little value, your time would have been better spent elsewhere? Large team meetings are notoriously hard to hold effectively—they often either feel like a series of announcements by management or a disorganized mess where most of what's being said doesn't seem relevant to your work objectives. Successful meetings are the responsibility of those calling them; strategies and pitfalls associated with meetings are discussed further in chapter 5 (see *Team Meeting Success* on page 159).

Influencing Team Structure

Remember that the above list of team types is not exhaustive—there are many variations on these as well as some entirely different structures to be found in project-focused organizations. So how is team structure decided upon? There are several influential factors:

- **Previous structures:** The single biggest influence on how an organization chooses to organize its project teams is the structures that precede it. This inertia can be hard to break, and the choice to try a new structure can be difficult to sell. There's also a strong possibility that the organization has arrived at the most appropriate structure through trial-and-error, making a switch less likely to succeed.

- **The culture of the organization:** Covered in chapter 1, organizational and team culture have a huge influence in all areas of decision making—how teams are structured bears no exception (see *Matching Leadership with Culture* on page 10).

- **Organizational and team processes:** There is an undeniable link between the way a team is expected to carry out its work and the structure of that team (for more, see *Values, Needs, and Process* on page 36).

- **The domain or industry:** The influence of the industry may be a matter of tradition, preference, or requirements and regulation. Using established structures common to the field can sometimes allow a team to avoid structural pitfalls that have already been accounted for by the "tribal knowledge" of their industry. Additionally, new employees may have worked at organizations with similar structures, making them more comfortable as members of their new team.

Now that we've considered both the larger structure of teams and the various factors that influence that structure, we can move into finer details: the roles of individual team members.

Common Team Roles

The building blocks of a team's structure are its *roles*—defined sets of expectations assigned to one or more individuals. It's important to note that these expectations are tied to the role, not the person; a role should be defined outside of whom it's assigned to, somewhat like a job description. The following are a few common team roles:

- **Team leader:** This role is responsible for guiding the project team towards the goal set before them. Team leaders will likely have varying levels of authority regarding what is and isn't to be accomplished, who is on the team, or the time and budget available. It's important they focus on what they *can* do rather than on their limitations. This role is a major focus of this book.

  Important skills include:

  - **Leadership:** The focus of chapter 1.
  - **Prioritization:** The focus of chapter 3.
  - **Communication:** The focus of chapter 5.

- **Information manager:** Projects include more than the product being built—they include all types of project artifacts and information along the way, including initial requirements/specifications, technical documentation, measurements, process information, reports, and much more. Information managers are responsible for this data in much the same way a warehouse manager is responsible for the goods in their care: information needs to be gathered, organized, stored, and distributed accurately, securely, and efficiently.

  Important skills include:

  - **Elicitation:** Gathering knowledge or information from stakeholders. In most projects, the most apparent form of elicitation is *requirements* or *specifications elicitation* (see *Defining Project Outcomes: A Layered Approach* on page 51).

  - **Organization:** Gathering and keeping project artifacts and information in a manner that is safe, error-free, and efficiently accessed. For most modern projects, this involves a database or file repository—these systems have their own skill requirements.

  - **Reporting:** Clearly and accurately distributing knowledge or information under their care. In most cases, this will include status on the expected project outcomes as well as information about the team and processes (see *Communicating with Metrics and Reports* on page 164).

- **Externally-facing:** Many projects include stakeholders external to the organization—customers and contractors are two examples of this. Externally-facing team members act as the intermediary between the inside and the outside of the team.

  Important skills include:

  - **Perception:** A keen awareness of others. Some say perception is a talent rather than a skill, but it's undeniable that externally-facing team members must be able to perceive the satisfaction, needs, and outlook of those outside the team or organization, especially customers.

  - **Communication:** Gathering and setting external expectations. While the majority of the team leader's communication is within the team and organization, the externally-facing team member(s) are primarily responsible for external (mostly customer) communication. In some cases this may involve "translation" between the inside and outside world, factoring in context, jargon, differing personalities, and legal requirements (see *Stakeholder Expectation Management* on page 171).

– **Negotiation:** Reaching agreement. As a subset of communication, negotiation comes into play when what external contractors and customers want doesn't match what the organization and team is willing to comply with. Many of the techniques associated with conflict management are useful tools for negotiation (covered later in this chapter starting on page 126).

- **Problem-solver:** This role is responsible for finding and solving difficult problems. In many cases, a problem-solver is brought in when it's determined that the team members who've encountered the problem aren't equipped to solve it or are more effectively utilized in continuing other work. Risks, covered in chapter 3 (page 97) are "future problems," and risk management will often fall under the domain of the problem-solver.

Important skills include:

– **Evaluation:** Fully perceiving the problem. The first step in solving any problem is understanding it: sometimes the root of the problem isn't apparent, and the problem-solver must identify all the factors involved. If a failed solution has already been tried, the problem-solver is responsible for articulating why it didn't work.

– **Research:** Efficient investigation around the problem. The path to a solution often requires more information than is immediately available. The problem-solver must learn the context surrounding the problem, seek similar problems and their solutions, and evaluate potential paths forward.

– **Implementation:** Engaging in the solution. Implementation involves creating a plan and executing it regardless of any obstacles (difficulties, complexities, etc.). In many ways, you could think of implementing the planned solution as a "mini-project."

- **Specialist:** Projects involve many different parts, many times reaching into a wide variety of domains. Specialists, also known as "subject matter experts" (SME's) or "technical specialists," are focused on a specific area of expertise in support of the project. Team members in this role may be responsible for completing work themselves or providing knowledge, training, and assistance to others.

Important skills include:

– **Evaluation:** Assessing the situation. Specialists need to be able to evaluate both the area of need and how they can provide assistance to the project team. This can be especially difficult if they're applying their knowledge to a new type of project or problem.

- **Anticipation:** Thinking about the future. Great specialists carefully consider what the project team is going to need and prepare these materials before they're asked to produce them. At the same time, just because someone is a specialist doesn't mean they know everything about a given subject; becoming an expert is much more about focus, forethought, and keeping abreast of important developments in the field.

- **Articulation:** Clearly communicating knowledge. Specialists often need to explain their expertise in a way that novices involved with the project can readily understand. This can take the form of face-to-face communication, working alongside team members, training, or written technical documentation.

What About the "Regular Team Member" Role?

What are some important skills for the "regular" members of a team? In addition to basic skills such as those required for the job (such as honesty and reliability), a team member must be able to properly interface with each of the other roles. Examples include:

- Obtaining clarity of direction from the team leader
- Knowing what to give to and ask for from information managers
- Gaining complete understanding through externally-facing team member(s)
- Awareness of when it's appropriate to bring in a problem-solver
- Understanding how to efficiently use each specialist's time

As previously stated, these are *roles*, not job titles. It's entirely possible that one person can be assigned to fill more than one role or that even roles are split between multiple team members. The first three, for example, are often filled by the project leader, especially in smaller projects, but just because a project leader chooses to fill all of these roles doesn't mean that they shouldn't consider the skills and techniques needed for each separately.

Now that we've considered the structure of a team and its success factors, it's time to consider how it grows and develops. The next section covers four basic stages of team development.

4.3 Team Development

So how does a young team grow to maturity? In 1965, Dr. Bruce Tuckman published a paper titled "Development sequence in small groups."[2] The central idea of the text was that all teams must progress through four stages as they grow to become productive: Forming, Storming, Norming, and Performing.

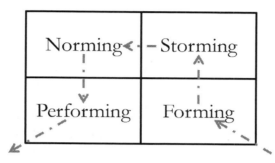

Forming

In this stage, the team comes together for the first time. This is when they learn about the goals or objectives they need to accomplish. At this point, each team member is completely independent and often chooses to act in a way that they feel is "appropriate" for their role, if yet defined.

Storming

As the name implies, this stage involves disagreements and personality clashes. Team members have begun to form opinions about other members' personalities and work habits, and a natural vying for leadership often ensues. Though this stage can be uncomfortable, it's often effective in helping the group choose a leader and establish the "rules" they'll operate under.

Norming

In this stage, the group of people really starts to self-identify as *team*. Personality clashes are resolved, social norms are established, and team members take collective ownership of the set of goals and objectives they've been tasked with.

Performing

Finally, the team is motivated, knowledgeable, and organized enough to start accomplishing its objectives. The team works, makes decisions, and often socializes as a group, acknowledging and even leveraging the diversity of individual members.

As a team progresses through the phases and ultimately becomes what they were assembled to be, it's important to remember that this is largely an internal process; the team must progress *organically*. While an experienced team leader knows and accepts the more difficult early stages, they also strive to create an environment that allows the team to reach the performing stage as soon as possible. Among other ways, a leader can achieve this by choosing team members who have compatible personalities, by understanding the role of conflict within a team (discussed later in this chapter), and by setting early, easily achievable goals that give the team members a sense of accomplishment strong enough to motivate them to continue through the project.

It's important to remember that just because a team has reached "performing" doesn't mean that it can't revert to an earlier stage of development. Conditions such as extreme stress or a changes in team makeup may cause this to happen. If this does occur, the team must again work through the stages and back up to efficient performing, though hopefully this happens quicker than the first time around.

Now that we've gained an understanding of the basic way a team develops, its structure, and essential elements of success, how do we ensure that a team has what it *needs*? In the next section, we'll introduce a model for understanding these needs.

4.4   Needs and the Team

Just like individuals, teams have basic needs. In his book *The Five Dysfunctions of a Team*, Patrick Lencioni lists five major needs: *Trust, Managed Conflict, Commitment, Accountability,* and *Results.*[3]

Like Maslow's hierarchy of needs, Lencioni's is also a hierarchical structure: the needs at the bottom must be addressed before those at the top. For instance, for a team to achieve *managed conflict*, it must first achieve an environment of *trust*. In the following sections, we'll explain each need and the best strategies and factors to consider in meeting it as a team.

4.5 Building Trust

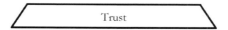

Trust is the foundation of teamwork. That being said, trust takes time. Though it's important for team members to trust each other interpersonally, what's even more important is that they trust for each other in the context of the group. This means that while they may not necessarily have confidence in each peer in every situation, they have enough faith in one another, in general, to cooperate professionally.

Basic professional trustworthiness only requires a history of positive interactions, but an outstanding team (i.e. "the next level") requires members to go beyond a strictly professional understanding of one another. It requires *vulnerability*. Many find this concept difficult. They see work as an environment immune from the strife and difficult emotions of their personal lives. After all, work always seems like a place that doesn't require emotional vulnerability. But this isn't true. In fact, the most successful teams sidestep this hesitation and share their vulnerability to appear more human. Because this hesitation often costs time, it's imperative that team leaders start moving their team toward vulnerability early on in team interactions, which will help everyone build and share trust.

For a leader, the most direct way to build trust is to allow their team team members to get to know them at a more interpersonal level. By being upfront about their likes, dislikes, hopes, and dreams outside work, the leader signals that this social environment is safe; this also encourages team members to follow suit. A word of caution: it's extremely important for the leader to encourage each team member to respect the vulnerability and confidentiality of others. One negative interaction can have devastating effects on the team's *reciprocal trust* for each member involved. To help achieve this, leaders need to set and enforce "ground rules," which form the basis for an emotional "safe zone."

Destroying Interpersonal Trust

Think about a time when you've felt that someone has violated your trust. What effect did this have on your ability to cooperate with that person? Similarly, think about a situation where you've violated the trust of someone else. What, if anything, did you do to resolve the situation? Some common examples of ways team members can violate the trust of others are covered as pitfalls in chapter 6 (see *Intellectual Violence* and *Loose Cannon* on page 182).

Setting a foundation of trust requires team members to understand the personalities of their peers—their values, motivations, and behavioral patterns. Increasingly, organizations have employed behavioral profiling activities ("personality tests") as a basis for this type of team development. Based on early work by Jung[4] and Marston,[5] examples of these include the DISC Assessment[6] and the Myers–Briggs Type Indicator.[7] These tests are often presented in a workshop format that includes the test itself, an analysis of individual results, and, most importantly, a group discussion between participants.

A Shorter "Personality Test"

Though not as comprehensive as many well-known tests, chapter 1 includes a basic set of questions designed to facilitate thought and discussion around your preferred leadership styles, types of influence, and motivators. Use this tool to learn your individual results, then consider using these results to participate group discussion, which will help you learn about your peers' personalities (see *Chapter Tool: Who We Are as Leaders* on page 17).

Once trust is established, other needs come into play. Remember that trust is the very foundation of a productive team. Eroding this layer can have very real consequences on those stacked above it.

4.6   Managing Conflict

For many leaders and team members, the "nightmare scenario" at their workplace involves coworkers engaged in *conflict*. Common sources of conflict include schedules, project priorities, resources, technical options or tools, administrative procedures, cost, personalities, along with hundreds of others based on your context. These conflicts may simply involve clashing personalities; they may be genuinely complex disagreements regarding the work at hand. Either way, many workers would rather avoid conflict in the first place.

Personalities aside, a mature project leader understands that *conflict is in fact necessary* and can be extremely productive. Because people can be passionate about their work (or project), leaders understand that passion can lead to disagreement, squabbling, and, in extreme situations, even regrettable behavior. What's more, successful projects and a good decision-making process both heavily rely heavily on regular, productive debate, which can appear as conflict. Debate and conflict are close relatives; both thrive in the productive work place, and the most successful leaders know how to strategize them to achieve productive ends.

Although conflict is necessary, it can be extremely uncomfortable at times. This is why the "Managed Conflict" building block sits directly on top of the "Trust" building block: if team members are to have regular and productive conflict, they need to trust each other. Part of the need for basic "ground rules," discussed in the last section, is the need for *conflict norms*—the "ground rules" of conflict. These rules may include:

- Debate should surround a decision yet to be made, not one that's already been decided.

- Focus on the debated topic—it's easy to wander to new disagreements that don't directly relate.

- Avoid non-contributing statements, rhetoric, or name-calling. These don't speak directly to the topic of debate. Note: *Building Trust* (the section preceding this one) cautions against violating the trust or confidentiality of fellow team members. When debate degrades into a personal dispute, opportunities to destroy trust become abundant—be extremely careful!

- Listen respectfully, talk softly, avoid defensiveness, and back up statements with factual examples or data when possible.

- Agree to reach *consensus*, and ensure that all parties agree to wholeheartedly support the resulting decision, regardless of whether they agree individually. It's important to distinguish consensus—in which all parties feel that their views have been properly considered before a decision is made—from a simple majority vote that doesn't always reflect every single voter's opinion (see *Group Consensus / Planning Poker Estimation* on page 82).

Conflict-Related Pitfalls
Discussed in chapter 6, certain "pitfalls" relate directly to many of the principles of dealing with conflict. Examples include *Blamestorming* (page 180), *Blowhard Jamboree* (page 180), *Poor Project Team/Stakeholder Relations* (page 183), and *Loose Cannon* (page 182).

In some cases, a conflict will escalate beyond the ability for self-resolution, and the project leader will be forced to intervene. Whether you're a project leader or a team member, understanding basic conflict resolution techniques and when each is appropriate is an important skill to develop.

Each of the following techniques may be applicable:

Confronting / Problem Solving

Often considered the optimal solution, directly confronting conflict is a method of problem solving and follows a standard process:

1. Define the real/root problem
2. Analyze the problem
3. Identify solutions
4. Choose a solution (this can be difficult)
5. Implement a solution
6. Review the solution, and confirm that it solved the problem and repeat if necessary

- **When it works:** When conflict needs to be solved "once and for all."
- **When it may not work:** Confronting the conflict is time consuming. When deadlines or danger are present, it may not be a good option.

Compromising

When compromising, each party makes concessions to the other, reaching a mutually-accepted conclusion.

- **When it works:** When each option is roughly equivalent, and no superior choice seems to exist. Compromising can often be the most expedient solution to conflict.

- **When it may not work:** In some cases, a two-option solution isn't optimal. It may cause parties to choose a subset of what they want rather than considering a mutually-beneficial third option, which leads to a "lose-lose" resolution.

Withdrawal / Avoidance

When disagreeing parties can't reach a conclusion, one or more choose to remove themselves from the situation and thus ends the conflict.

- **When it works:** This technique works best when the conflict is personality-based or trivial rather than an actual, significant debate pertinent to the project. In some cases, postponement may be beneficial (i.e. time to change emotional states, intervention by another party is needed, or a "cooling off" period all may help).
- **When it may not work:** When the parties in conflict need to work closely together, especially if time-critical work is needed for the success of the project.

Smoothing / Accommodating

As the name implies, smoothing involves placing the concerns of others before your own.

- **When it works:** Accommodating a stakeholder who's extremely important to the health of the project. Smoothing also can allow time for both parties to think over the situation at hand. It also has the potential to work if the issue is less important to one party than the other; the party who's has less concerned with the issue concedes to the other.
- **When it may not work:** Accommodating, like compromise, leaves at least one party unsatisfied. This could damage the project down the line, and there's also the potential for the accommodated party to abuse the other party. In addition, some people see smoothing as a sign of weakness, and may be offended by it.

Collaborating

Often considered an optimal solution for conflict resolution, collaborating involves conflicting parties working together to find a solution that satisfies everyone; the result is often a previously unconsidered third option.

- **When it works:** Collaborating can work especially

well when more than two parties are involved. Reasonable, non-emotional demeanor is best, as is an environment in which parties have a high level of trust for each other.

- **When it may not work:** Collaboration often takes longer than other conflict-resolution techniques, so a looming deadline, impending threat, untrusting parties, or unknown agendas can make it impractical or frustrating for all involved.

Forcing

Forcing involves an authority figure making a decision and forcing an end to the conflict.

- **When it works:** A deadline or danger requires a quick decision or immediate resolution to the conflict. Forcing is also appropriate when one party's position or plan violates rules or ethical standards. It has possible value as a last-resort option.
- **When it may not work:** Forcing often doesn't resolve the conflict—it can leave the problem largely unsolved, with the potential still there for the conflict to reappear at an even more inopportune time in the future.

Although trust and conflict resolution are the foundation of a team's needs, by themselves they typically aren't enough to create a productive team environment. The next three, commitment, accountability, and results are where "the rubber meets the road" for a project team.

4.7   Achieving Commitment

Individual commitment to a group effort—that is what makes a team work, a company work, a society work, a civilization work. – Vince Lombardi[8]

As it relates to the team, commitment has many dimensions, each of which involves the central idea of commitment, but from a host of different angles:

- The leader's commitment to the team
- The leader's commitment to the project
- The team's commitment to the leader
- The team's commitment to the project
- An individual team member's commitment to the team
- An individual team member's commitment to the project
- The team's commitment to being a team
- Individual commitments that the team or members make to decisions, tasks, or deadlines

Ultimately all of these are commitments, but how each affects the health of a team or project varies wildly. One common thread running through all of them is the concept of *clarity*. In order to achieve commitment, it must be clear what the team or individual is committing to. Tools that assist in achieving and perpetuating this clarity include meeting notes, lists of action items, and artifacts such as project requirements and schedules. Contracts, another common project document, personify a commitment between two parties.

The Leader's Commitment
The leader's commitment to the team and the project objectives represents the most obvious, upfront commitment in any project; a leader's lack of commitment will almost certainly lead to a disastrous end. As discussed in chapters 1 through 3, project leadership represents a continuous commitment to the organization, promotion, and prioritization of project objectives, tasks, team members, and stakeholders.

In addition to the practical needs that the leader's commitment satisfies, a leader's perceived lack of commitment will often lead team members to lower and even stop prioritizing project work. This is especially true in functional organizations (see *Functional Organizations* on page 31) or organizations that have more than one project happening simultaneously. If team members' time and attention are split, they'll be more likely to spend time working with leaders who are demonstrably engaged in their leadership duties. Ultimately, team members function better—because they're more focused—under the direction of an engaged leader.

The Organization's Commitment to a Project
What about an organization's commitment level to the project? Often, it may seem like a project leader or team can't do much about an organization's commitment to a project; the organization itself must establish and demonstrate a level of commitment. The most apparent indica-

tors of low commitment include a restrictive budget or deadline and a lack of resources. Less obvious indicators could include lower executive interest, lower team morale, or a spike in the number of project risks including a seemingly higher chance of project cancellation. When gauging an organization's commitment level consider this: an organization is really represented by its leaders—are there one or more management stakeholders whom you can positively influence for the success of the project?

Finally, project leaders must consider their individual passion for the project. Across a leader's career, it's likely they will end up leading projects that don't excite them, or even worse, that they even find unnecessary and "beneath them." In this situation, the leader must constantly monitor their own attitude along with how they're leading the project; a disinterested or unmotivated leader can quickly and unknowingly create a toxic team environment.

The Team's Commitment

A successful project team is one that values commitment: commitment to the project, its completion, and its schedule, all while carrying out the trials and practices necessary to remain a strong team. A team with "commitment problems" will often seem dispassionate, seek to place blame, steer discussion towards their perceived need for more resources, and debate seemingly insignificant details. When these types of problems arise, the success of the team will often be dictated by one or two individuals only (see *Heroics* on page 181).

To strengthen a team's commitment, it's important for a team leader to understand the following:

- **Trust and conflict management:** At the team level, commitment requires the foundational needs that appear below it in the pyramid: trust and conflict management (previously discussed in this chapter).

- **Clear prioritization:** This is necessary for the team to know what to commit to. It's impossible for the team to commit to everything at once. As such, a team's leader must order and lay out priority (see chapter 3: *Prioritization: The Core of Project Leadership*).

- **A relatively healthy team:** This is required for commitment to the project. If the team is forced to focus on internal problems or has internal issues such as a destructive team member (see *Loose Cannon* on page 182), external commitments become a lower priority, which is detrimental to the team's success.

- **Good team structure:** Structure such as clear roles and responsibilities, standardized procedures for documenting decisions, and a clear vision and group identity are all essential for commitment (see *Team Structure* earlier in this chapter).

By intentionally prioritizing the catalysts of commitment and by recognizing and remedying weaknesses, a focused team leader becomes the promoter of a team that understands and values commitment. In short, a team leader should try to make commitment a part of the team's culture. They should strive to build trust, ensure that decisions (and their consequences) are clear to all, reward good work, and learn from failure.

In some rare cases, all of these conditions are present and the leader only needs to *ask* for commitment from the team, a strategy that has a much higher chance of success if the team already thinks highly of them (see *Influence* on page 5).

It's important to remember that not every individual team member must agree with a decision or plan of action for that team to be committed. Rather, each team member's level of commitment to the team must be high enough so that they place the value of commitment above that of individual disagreement.

The Individual Team Member's Commitment

Because of the nature of interpersonal relationships, at times it can be quite easy to identify weak commitment levels from individual team members: frequent excuses, tardiness, argumentative behavior, and blaming others for failures are all symptoms to look for. A lack of commitment can also be seen in their work as well; work products will often be "just good enough," turned in right before (or shortly after) the deadline, and will often not include input from other team members. Overall, their work may lack ownership and vision.

In many ways, the reasons for an individual's lack of commitment mirror those of a team's. Often, individuals' lack of commitment inspire the group's lack of commitment to each other, and eventually to a project. How a project leader can inspire commitment from an individual, however, is distinct from how a team is inspired. Tactics may include:

- **Communicating commitments with more clarity:** Perhaps the individual isn't aware of how important this project or their portion of this project actually is?

- **Seeking the reason for a lack of commitment:** This could be because of work or personal problems. Seek the whole truth and any extenuating circumstances before making assumptions.

- **Assigning leadership/ownership:** Although it may seem counterintuitive, a lack of individual commitment sometimes stems from a feeling of powerlessness. Assigning direct ownership of results may remedy this.

- **Recognition of achievement:** Recognize the areas that the individual is showing commitment to or excelling in. Remember that peer recognition is a powerful motivator (see page 7).

- **Engaging the team member's creativity:** Find elements of the project that may inspire them to seek new and creative solutions. Autonomy and interesting work is another primary motivator (see page 8).

Often, the most successful way to increase an individual's commitment involves the leader taking direct responsibility for that team member (a commitment of their own). One-on-one time, coaching, and developing a personal connection may lead to renewed success, especially if that particular team member is essential to the project's success overall. Unfortunately, a team member who fails to commit to the team or project over the long term can be toxic—at that point, it may be necessary to replace them.

Your Commitment to the Team and Project
Think about a project that you've participated in as a team member (not a leader). Were you more committed to the team or to the project? What undermined your motivation and commitment? Did your leader inspire commitment? Was the team or project successful?

Whether it's the individual team member, the leader, or the team in its entirety, commitment is essential to productivity. When combined with *accountability*, which is covered in the next section, teams can begin to look into the future for completion of tasks and the project at large rather than being forced to remain in the here-and-now.

4.8 Embracing Accountability

As we move up the pyramid, it becomes increasingly apparent that the steps below (in this case: commitment, managed conflict, and trust) are vital. The majority of articles and resources addressing accountability in a team directly mention each of these concepts. In a 2014 Harvard Business Review article entitled "The Best Teams Hold Themselves Accountable," the authors highlight how important it is to build an environment in which team members resolve their own conflicts without requiring a leader to intervene.[9] This article states that stronger teams hold themselves internally *accountable* rather than relying on the leader to police them.

But what is team accountability? As an individual, we think about accountability as our readiness to accept responsibility for our actions or decisions, but we should broaden this perspective to include *whom* we're accountable to. Inside a team, understanding what accountability looks like requires us to consider all angles:

- **Accountability to the leader:** This is the most natural type of accountability because it's what people most often experience. The leader often has formal, reward, or coercive influence over the team member (see *Influence* on page 5). This is the most important type of accountability in top-down team structures (page 114).

- **Accountability to oneself:** Otherwise known as *self-motivation*, a team member's "relationship with oneself" is essential. Distractions or difficulties in one's personal life can have a ripple effect on accountability.

- **Accountability to one's peers:** This is the most essential form of accountability, because instead of feeling accountable to one person (the leader or oneself), this motivation comes from the entire team. It's essential that each team member feel equally accountable to each other; inequality can cause difficult problems in the group dynamic. The interdisciplinary team structure is built entirely around peer-to-peer accountability (page 115).

Within a healthy team environment, accountability among peers is the most reliable of the three options. Accountability to one's self and to one's "boss" has more potential to break down due to the single relationship involved: more relationships mean more accountability.

So what practices can a leader introduce to foster peer-to-peer accountability? The easiest and most successful is simply to add a regular review of accomplishments to the natural cycle the team is following. By giving team members a chance to address what has and hasn't been done in a team forum, they're forced to honestly evaluate their level of commitment against that of others. Methods that emphasize peer accountability strongly encourage leaders to create frequent opportunities for this to occur—many Agile processes, for example, employ a "daily stand-up meeting" in which each team member is asked the question, "What did you accomplish since the last meeting?" (a more thorough description of *Daily Stand-Up Meetings* is available on page 205).

Ultimately, it remains the team leader's responsibility to introduce accountability, but the team itself must work to *embrace* that accountability. Even though the leader, who often reports to management or other higher-ups, is *assigned* accountability, it's up to the entire team to *choose* to be accountable to each other.

Both commitment and accountability require *clarity* for team members. Commitment requires the clarity of trust (the lowest rung on the pyramid)—knowing others well enough to commit to being a team together. Accountability requires clarity of information: *What* am I accountable for, and *who* am I accountable to? A perfect tool that helps teams figure out who is responsible to whom and for what is the "RASCI":

The "RASCI" Accountability Matrix

Though trust, managed conflict, and commitment are important elements of any project, accountability is where the *specific* tasks and responsibilities of the project meet the team members (as individuals or as roles). In some cases, it's unclear who is accountable for what; in others, someone is accountable but is unaware of their commitment level. A tool for directly addressing this is the *accountability matrix*.

Deemed especially useful for disambiguating complex multi-task/multi-role projects, the RASCI plots tasks/responsibilities against roles by assigning one or more of the following acronymic letters:

Responsible: This is the person or role who is to complete the task or fulfill the responsibility. If more than one party has the "R," the varying levels of responsibility are often assigned by the person with the "A."

Accountable: This is the role or person who is ultimately answerable for proper completion of the task or accountable if a responsibility isn't fulfilled. Each task, action, or responsibility should have exactly one "A."

Support: A subset of "R," support roles may be called in when help is needed to complete the task or responsibility. The "R" role knows who is assigned to help if needed.

Consulted: These parties are often specialists or subject matter experts (see the *Specialist* role on page 121) who may be called upon to provide input or expertise when needed.

Informed: It is important these parties be kept up to date on the status of the task or responsibility, especially if significant changes to scope or schedule are made. This party should also be informed when the task is completed.

A visual example can be seen below. Note that roles are placed along the top row and can include more than one person. Activities or responsibilities are placed in the left column.

	Project Manager	Project Sponsor	Engineers	Tester 1
Responsibility X	A	I	R	
Activity 1	A	S		
Responsibility Y	C	R		A
Activity 2	R, A			C
Task Alpha	A	R	S	

RASCI: Rental Property

Look at the grid on the next page. Think about how each role might be involved in each real-estate related task, and then place the letters R,A,S,C, and I as appropriate. In addition to the tasks listed, create a new one and place the letters as appropriate. Finally, eliminate the "Property Manager" role by placing an "X" over the entire column and

reassign or reprioritize the letters previously included for that role.

	Real Estate Salesperson	Property Owner	Tenant	Property Manager	Contractor
Find Property					
Find Tenant					
Pay Rent					
Maintain Property					

RASCI: Your Project

Using the format above, create a RASCI for a project which you're currently participating in. Remember that the roles may be groups of people rather than just one individual. Choose some key activities or tasks to include, and try to think of ones that would force dissimilar letter assignments.

Because it's such a nebulous concept, accountability is tough to measure. The currency of accountability is *results*, the very top of the pyramid, which we'll discuss in the next section.

4.9   Focusing on Results

Chances are, when you think of a successful team, you think about a team's *results*. Often, we think that results are a natural outcome of a strong, well-led team. They become a natural byproduct of why the team was created in the first place, right?

It's hard to imagine just how many essential needs must be met before a team can focus on the reason for its very existence and start producing solid results. But regardless of which stage or level of needs a team has reached, it's likely achieved *some sort* of results, usually the work products it's produced. But even these may merely be the results of individual efforts (see *Heroics* on page 181). Think of it this way: An undeveloped team has a similar output to the same number of people working independently and only occasionally handing work off to others. This type of team, however, doesn't usually produce high-quality results because it's not achieving the efficiency only a well-developed team will experience.

By addressing all of their core needs (trust, managed conflict, commitment, and accountability), the team can change its internal focus to an external one: results. The team leader, who was previously focused mostly on nurturing the internal structures and health of the team, can now emphasize a different set of responsibilities:

- **Prioritization:** Because the team can now effectively and efficiently produce results, the leader must constantly decide which tasks and objectives are the most important. Many efforts are wasted without proper prioritization (see chapter 3, *Prioritization: The Core of Project Leadership*).

- **Clarification:** To keep the team from running in the wrong direction, tasks and objectives must be "crystal clear." Because there's usually less lead time ahead of the team's work products, more "pre-work" may be needed to ensure the team understands what is to be done.

- **Visibility:** In addition to their individual tasks and objectives, each team member must see the bigger picture of their project—it becomes important to specify and reflect on the end product the team is moving towards. This is because an efficient and results-focused team needs less micromanagement— it makes decisions related to its objectives quickly and efficiently. Increasing visibility helps everyone keep a sharp focus on the final destination.

  Another element of visibility relates to the team members themselves. They must choose to put the profile and health of the team above their own. An individual focus on status or an ego-driven, credit-seeking atmosphere can be extremely destructive to a focus on results because the team members instead focus on individual recognition (often called "playing office politics").

- **Process:** Instead of many independent workers completing tasks and then handing them off, a results-focused team is more akin to a well-oiled machine, with its many parts working together in harmony. The interconnected nature of this metaphor demonstrates the benefits of a clear process. Although some would argue that process must already be in place even before reaching this point, it's important for the project leader to realize that the processes themselves should be documented and communicated throughout the project. This is critically important when trying to substitute team members while keeping the positive momentum that's already in place (see *Values, Needs, and Process* on page 36).

Though the notion of "results" changes from project to project and team to team, a team that has a laser-focus on results is a remarkable sight to see. Those who have participated in this type of team often reminisce on the successful amalgamation of *trust*, *managed conflict*, *commitment*, *accountability*, and the *results focus* that contributed to this powerful experience.

4.10   Chapter Tool: Evaluating Your Team's Maturity

The concepts covered in this chapter lend themselves to evaluating a team, from its developmental stages through whether its needs are properly fulfilled. But have you ever considered the *maturity* of your team? While not scientific, the evaluation below can help you, the team leader, and team members reflect on your team's overall maturity.

Team Development Maturity Evaluation
On a piece of paper, quickly and honestly answer each of the questions below. Once you've completed all of the questions, "score" your answers based on the information from page 143 and consider what the results may mean regarding your team's developmental maturity. This test can be taken by either the leader or a team member, and, if they're honest with themselves, they should get similar results.

1. My team:

   (a) Has little or no distinct identity when compared to others in the organization

   (b) Feels it's a team but struggles at times with identity

   (c) Draws strength from its strong sense of identity and purpose

2. Regarding goals:

(a) Each team member doesn't seem to connect their individual objectives with those of other team members

(b) Team members understand that a group effort is needed to succeed at some types of work

(c) The team knows what its goals are and benefits from sharing a strong common purpose in achieving them

3. The majority of time:

    (a) The team seems to have very little self-awareness

    (b) A good portion of the team is aware of problems or needs it's facing

    (c) The team is aware of and capitalizes on its strengths and actively works towards improving its weaknesses

4. Individuals on the team:

    (a) Work more-or-less independently—the only defined role is the team leader's

    (b) Don't have written roles, but are aware of and capitalize on each other's specialties

    (c) Have multiple, formally-defined roles and understand why each is important

5. Regarding team "rules":

    (a) There are no "rules" set by the team—each individual behaves as they feel they should

    (b) The team recognizes that "rules" are important, but is still in the process of defining them

    (c) Each team member is aware and in support of what is appropriate for the team—the "rules" are well known by all

6. As it relates to team members' view of each other:

    (a) Team members don't seem to trust each other at all

    (b) Team members trust each other in a professional setting as colleagues

    (c) It's obvious that each team member trusts both the leader and each other interpersonally as well as professionally

7. Regarding conflict, my team:

    (a) Avoids conflict at all cost because once it starts, it's hard for the team to remain productive

    (b) Gets uncomfortable at times because of conflict, but prioritizes resolving things quickly

    (c) Values and encourages metered, fair debate, even if it risks conflict

8. When trying to make a decision:

    (a) After some unproductive debate, the team leader generally has the final say—the "winning" party feels superior to the "losing" party

    (b) Disagreeing parties can usually compromise; if not, one party cedes to the other because it's not as important to them

    (c) Team members prefer to collaborate and work through the problem-solving process—if one party doesn't agree with a decision, they still support it wholeheartedly

9. The team leader:

    (a) Seems primarily committed to their own success; a successful project may be a part of this

    (b) Is fully committed to and has taken ownership of the success of the project even if it may not help their career

    (c) Regularly demonstrates commitment to the success of individual team members, and knows a successful project will help everyone involved

10. Within most projects:

    (a) Priorities and team structure seem to change daily, and team members are often unsure what they should commit to

    (b) Though difficulties do happen, team members have a good idea of what's important and are obviously committed to the project's success

    (c) The team actively seeks and obtains clarity, commits to its work, and follows the commitment to completion with little supervision

11. Team members seem primarily accountable to:

    (a) The leader or boss

    (b) Themselves—they're very self-motivated

    (c) Their fellow team members

12. The team achieves:

    (a) Less or about what the team members would achieve independently

    (b) A good amount because team members recognize who is best suited for each task and pass them off to each other

    (c) A surprising amount because the team works, makes decisions, and delivers in ways that astound those around them

Team Development Maturity Evaluation Results

How did your team do? You've most likely noticed that for each question, "a" represented the most immature team, "c" the most mature, and "b" somewhere in between. Notes for each question:

1. Self-identification as a team is an important part of growing more productive (basic types of teams are listed on page 114).
2. Common purpose and goals are a key to successful teams (page 112).
3. Self-awareness is vital if a team is going to improve itself (several influencers of team structure are listed on page 118).
4. Team roles are important, and formally defining them shows that the team is thinking about its future (page 119).
5. Team "rules," also known as norms, are defined as a team develops. In Tuckman's model, they don't exist yet in "forming," they are debated in "storming," and are finalized in "norming" (page 123).
6. Trust is the most basic of team needs. Interpersonal trust is the most advanced form (page 125).
7. Managed conflict is an important team need and debate is a valuable tool (page 126).
8. Decision making can often be a source of conflict. Some conflict resolution techniques, such as collaboration, are generally considered as consistently better solutions (several techniques are listed

starting on page 128).

9. The most mature team leader is committed to the project and to the team, not just to themselves (page 130).

10. Commitment, one of the basic team needs, requires *clarity* so that the team and all its members know what they're committing to (page 131).

11. Larger accountability structures (to peers rather than to leaders, for example) capitalize the concept of teams (page 135).

12. Results are the ultimate measure of a team. A mature team is more than the sum of its parts (page 138).

4.11   Summary and Conclusion

Successful team leadership goes beyond understanding the basics covered in chapter 1 (*Understanding Leadership*). There are several factors that contribute to the success of a team, such as complimentary skillsets, common purpose, and good planning. Understanding the structure of teams is also important, including some basic ways teams are organized, why they're arranged the way they are, and the roles that are important in those arrangements.

Many experts study the way teams develop as well as what needs are essential in that development. Team members' trust in their peers and conflict management, for example, are basic needs that must be met before more advanced concepts such as commitment and accountability come into play. The ultimate measure of any team is its results: does what the team produces justify the time, energy, and resources needed to create and sustain it?

Though a team is composed of roles, a major theme of this text is the *people* behind those roles—especially what a leader can do to help them achieve their best as a resource and a team member. Communication is an essential part of every aspect of team structure and development, and we'll focus on it in more detail in the next chapter.

Key Terms

Accountability: A readiness to accept responsibility. Accountability usually involves another person or group, such as the leader or fellow team members (page 135).

Accountability Matrix: A table containing responsibilities on one axis and roles on the other, with indication of level of accountability in their intersections. An example is the "RASCI" (page 136).

Collaboration: A *conflict* resolution technique in which all parties work together to find a mutually-satisfactory resolution (page 129).

Commitment: The act of dedicating efforts or loyalty to a leader, team, project, or course of action. This requires clarity of what is being committed to (page 130).

Compromise: A *conflict* resolution technique in which each party makes concessions to the other (page 128).

Conflict: A disagreement between individuals or groups. Within a project, conflict isn't necessarily bad, but should be properly managed (page 126).

Consensus: An agreement within a team. Note that all individuals may not *fully* agree, but should still support the decision made by the team (page 127).

Forcing: A *conflict* resolution technique in which one party or someone in authority asserts a decision to end the debate or conflict (page 130).

Forming: The first stage in Tuckman's team development model in which team members come together for the first time (page 123).

Interdisciplinary Team: A group of people with varied skills or expertise who work together to accomplish project objectives (page 115).

Norming: The third stage in Tuckman's team development model in which "rules" are finally established and attention is turned to the work at hand (page 123).

Performing: The fourth and last stage in Tuckman's team development model. The team has established itself and is fully focused on completing its objectives (page 123).

Problem Solving: Confronting a problem via a process that includes defining, analyzing, solving, and confirming the solution to the problem. Considered an optimal *conflict* resolution technique (page 128).

Results: The achievement of goals and objectives and the eventual outcome of productive work. The focus of a mature team (page 138).

Role: A defined set of expectations assigned to one or more individuals. These expectations persist regardless of who is assigned to the role (page 119).

Smoothing: Also known as accommodating, a *conflict* resolution technique in which one party puts the wishes or concerns of another before their own (page 129).

Specialist: A team member (role) who concentrates on or has superior knowledge and skill in a particular field (page 121).

Storming: The second stage in Tuckman's team development model. Characterized by sometimes chaotic efforts to define roles and formal or informal "rules" (page 123).

Trust: A team member's ability to rely on or have confidence in others. Trust is the most fundamental team need (page 125).

Withdrawal: A less-than-optimal *conflict* resolution technique where one or more parties remove themselves from the disagreement. (page 129).

Review Questions

1. A team attributes its success primarily to complimentary skillsets. Which type of team structure does it most likely follow?

2. Which category of team enjoys solving difficult problems?

3. Which type of team will most likely have its members primarily focus on the "boss"?

4. You and a colleague are both part of a large, variable structure team but have never worked together directly. What strategy should you use when considering him or her?

5. What are three important skills needed by the information manager role?

6. Your team seems to have resolved most disagreements and is starting to shift concern to the objectives you've been given. Which stage of Tuckman's Model for Team Development is this team experiencing?

7. Your team has reached deadlock regarding a major decision with a quickly-approaching deadline. Which resolution technique is a better fit: collaborating or forcing?

8. Which three parties/entities need to enter into commitments for a successful team experience?

9. Of the three "angles" of accountability, which is unique to the team experience?

10. When using a "RASCI" accountability matrix, which letter must be assigned to at least one party for each task or responsibility?

Exercises

1. Name a famous team (examples: Cirque du Soleil, the USPS, Plato and Socrates). What major factors played a role in its successes? How is it structured? Did this team include defined roles?

2. You're in the process of creating a new team for a high-profile project within your division. You feel that the typical structure in the industry is a top-down team, but your company's culture seems to prefer interdisciplinary teams. What additional information would you need to make this decision? How would you support your decision to naysayers?

3. Choose two of the factors in the *What Makes a Team Successful?* section (starting on page 111). For each, explain how this success factor would contribute to each of the four team structures listed starting on page 114.

4. You are tasked with creating an interdisciplinary team for an important technical project slated to start in the next quarter. Other than their aptitude in specific skill areas, what properties would you look for? During interviews, how would you measure these properties in your candidates?

5. Your 7-member engineering team has been in Tuckman's "performing" stage for over a month. Unfortunately, recent reorganization of the company has reassigned two of your team members to another division. The addition of two replacements has resulted in your team reverting to the "storming" stage. As the team leader, what strategies can you employ to help your team reach the "performing" stage once again?

6. Thinking about a recent team experience, what are some personality traits that you find difficult to relate to? What could members of the team who have these traits do to increase your level of trust?

7. Two businesses share a single shopping-plaza-style parking lot, and they have recently been unhappy with each other regarding how their respective employees and customers park. Choose three conflict-management techniques (which start on page 128)—how could the businesses employ each successfully? List assumptions about the scenario as needed.

8. Look at the leadership styles listed in chapter 1 starting on page 3. For each, which is most important for individuals: commitment to the leader, the team, or the project? Why?

9. Using the format illustrated on page 137, create a RASCI for a basic hotel operation. Be sure to include at least 5 parties (Desk Clerk, Maid, etc.) and 5 areas of potential responsibility (quality of room, reservations, etc.).

10. You feel that your team has reached a point where it increasingly requires clarity and visibility for team members. How would you change a weekly team meeting to accommodate these new priorities? Give specific examples of how elements of the meeting would look before and after the change.

Notes

[1]Larson, Carl E. and Frank M. LaFasto. *Teamwork: What Must Go Right, What Can Go Wrong.* Newbury Park, CA: SAGE. 1989.

[2]Tuckman, Bruce. "Developmental sequence in small groups". Psychological Bulletin. 63 (6). p 384–99. 1965.

[3]Lencioni, Patrick. *The Five Dysfunctions of a Team: A Leadership Fable.* San Francisco: Jossey-Bass, 2002.

[4]Jung, C. G. *Collected works of C. G. Jung, Volume 6 - Third Edition.* Princeton, NJ: Princeton University Press. 1971. First appeared in German in 1921.

[5]Marston, William Moulton. *Emotions of Normal People.* London: K. Paul, Trench, Trubner & Co. Ltd, 1928.

[6]DiSC, various examples [Measurement instrument]. John Wiley & Sons, Inc. Available from multiple vendors, listed at http://everythingdisc.com/. Retrieved 2017.

[7]Myers, Isabel Briggs, Mary H. McCaulley, Naomi Quenk, and Allan Hammer. *MBTI Handbook: A Guide to the development and use of the Myers-Briggs Type Indicator - Third Edition.* Consulting Psychologists Press. 1998.

[8]Lombardi, Vince. "Quotes | Vince Lombardi". VinceLombardi.com. http://www.vincelombardi.com/quotes.html. January 2010.

[9]Grenny, Joseph. *The Best Teams Hold Themselves Accountable. Harvard Business Review.* Harvard Business Review May 30, 2014. https://hbr.org/2014/05/the-best-teams-hold-themselves-accountable. Accessed May 2017.

Communication and Expectation Management

In this chapter, we address the mechanics of team communication, meeting success, and the ethics of communication. To do this, we focus on the importance of "expectation management" as well as how to achieve appropriate communication when including metrics and reports.

E very relationship advice book, column, or blog seems to have one thing in common: they all tout the importance of communication. Though few would dispute the truth of this, there seem to be far fewer answers than questions when it comes to success in project communication. What should I say? When? To whom? How often? By which method? In this chapter, we will discuss general answers to these questions; since the specifics of your project will vary, this chapter provides some of the global methods and tools that will help you apply these concepts to your individual project and team.

5.1   The Importance of Project Communication

Project communication used to be relatively simple. In days-gone-by, a product may have been produced by two people—an artisan and their apprentice. A customer placed an order, and one or two people completed the work. Coopers built barrels, blacksmiths made horseshoes, and so on. During these exchanges, communication tended to be face-to-face and one-on-one. When the industrial revolution changed the nature of production, face-to-face communication moved towards the unidirectional communication of mass-marketing: a corporation produced a product and advertised its benefits via disconnected media such as magazines and television.

In the modern era, however, this is no longer the case, especially as it relates to product engineering and our service-based economy. Modern project teams are as big as their projects are complex. Mass-customization and complicated, custom-built projects are no longer the exception, but the rule. To this end, market response is critical—companies increasingly base marketing and product decisions on actual consumer feedback, whether direct or through social media. Gone as well are the strict, clear hierarchical structures of the master-apprentice or even the top-down foreman-factory worker model. Modern organizations are much flatter, more responsive, and more likely to employ professionals who expect to be much more mobile throughout their careers.

These changes have broadened the emphasis on two-way, responsive communication within teams, both at the organizational and customer levels. Within a team, responsiveness to change is both expected and welcomed. Within an organization, leaders need to properly demonstrate their vision vertically to management as well as horizontally to their peers. Outside the team, many stakeholders also expect more direct involvement throughout the process—a condition made necessary by market forces and increased competitive pressure. Indeed, it is often difficult to determine *who* the team is, and which personnel are strictly stakeholders; individuals will often shift between the two based on timing and perspective (see *Who We Lead* on page 12 and *Team Structure* on page 114).

5.2   Basic Communication Concepts

The complexity of project communication is a result of many sources: the number of people/parties we must communicate with, the methods of communication, the variations in types of communication, and the potential blockers to that communication. Each of these can be magnified by the complex and multidisciplinary nature of most project teams.

The Complexity of Multiple Channels

A *communication channel* is simply a path through which communication must travel.[1] In the example on the next page, there are 6 channels among 4 team members.

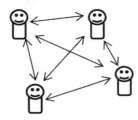

It makes sense—each team member must maintain a communication channel with every other team member. But what if we introduce a new person to the team?

The illustrations make it clear that adding one more person adds many more channels—all of which need to be monitored, maintained, and regularly clarified. By adding just two new team members, we've already added 9 more channels [(n(n-1))/2]. This presents a need for the project leader to consider not only how many channels exist in total, but also which communication channels should be managed more closely. Because of the issues presented in this scenario, many experts believe that there is a practical limit to how large a functioning team can be.[2]

Levels of complexity are further enhanced when multiple teams work together. In these situations, project leaders must make decisions about the number of channels that their teams will maintain with others outside of the team. In some cases, the best course of action may be for the project leader themselves to act as a "single point of entry/exit" for all outside communication. If not properly thought out, this can result in a "single point of failure" if the leader is absent or a poor communicator—a grave risk to the project's success (see *Risk Management* on page 97). (Chapter 4's discussion of common team structures includes a potential "externally-facing" role, which takes responsibility for this type of communication. See page 120.)

Channels of Communication

In the previous illustrations, each arrow represents a channel of communication. Though we may assume that this means a face-to-face conversation, reality tells us otherwise; in the modern world, there are literally dozens of communication *mediums* available to us at any given time.

- Face-to-Face
- Message Boards
- Social Media
- Multi-Channel
- Online Video Posts
- Text Messages

- Email
- Video Conference
- Postal Mail
- Television
- Print Media
- Photo Sharing

- Instant Messages
- Written Notes
- Advertisement
- Telephone
- Blogs
- and many more

Because so many potential channels exist, a project leader must be careful to strategically choose channels properly based on both what is being said and how it should be perceived. A simple example is illustrated by the phrase "a picture is worth a thousand words"—if a picture is needed to communicate the particular message, certain channels are immediately eliminated. Additionally, differences exist in how channels are perceived and whether they are even viable options. Mass communication such as billboards and automobile recall notices are seen as less "personal" and may also be ignored by their receivers. Highly specialized communication such as handwritten notes or one-on-one phone calls have the potential to be prohibitively expensive if a wide audience is addressed.

Types of Communication

In addition to a myriad of channels, there are also dozens of *types* of communication. The type of communication you choose to use can have a huge effect on how that communication is received. Essentially, the type of communication as well as the medium or channel chosen is a part of the message itself. Some include:

- **Internal/External:** These communications vary based on whom they are directed to. External (to the organization, team, etc.) communications tend to be more formal.

- **Formal/Informal:** "Official," formal communications often require much more work and approval. "Unofficial," informal communications usually adopt an interpersonal tone.

- **Vertical/Horizontal:** The way that "higher-ups" are addressed often varies widely from the way team members communicate with one another. In the case of a project leader, vertical communication could include management or important stakeholders, and horizontal could include colleagues or other project groups. Peer-to-peer communication is typically horizontal and less formal.

- **Written/Oral:** These two common types of communication can have very different implications, especially down the line. Written communication is often considered more permanent whereas oral communication can be more appropriate in certain situations. Which of these you choose to use may have a big effect on how the message is perceived and may even carry legal repercussions down the road.

- **Verbal/Nonverbal/Paralingual:** When we communicate, our messages are influenced both by what we say and *how we sat it.* Verbal communication is almost always accompanied by nonverbal (posture, gestures, expression, etc.) and paralingual (pitch, tone of voice, channel, etc.) cues. Other types of communication may or may not include these (for example, is typing in ALL CAPS considered shouting?).

With so many channels, types, and different parties with which we communicate, the potential exists for breakdowns, also known as *communication blockers.*

Potential Communication Blockers

The genesis of a communication is an *idea.* Generally the goal of the communicator, or *sender,* is to choose from the channels available to them, *encode* a particular message, and send it through the selected channel. It then becomes their sincere hope that the *receivers* of that message properly understand, or *decode,* the original idea.

Unfortunately that channel or medium of communication may be fraught with danger. At the most basic level, technical issues could exist—static, broken connections, and other physical glitches can interfere with the delivery or clarity of a message. These types of issues are the least destructive to the original idea the sender wished to communicate because they are generally easier to solve and more detectable as they occur. The real difficulty lies in the sender's ability to encode the message in a way that is readily decodable by the receiver in spite of blockers. Examples of blockers could include:

- **Obvious Communication Blockers**
  - Language or cultural differences

  – Interruptions by other parties

  – Technical breakdowns

  – Distractions to one or both parties such as fatigue

- **Less Obvious Communication Blockers**

  – Negativity or hostility between the sender and the receiver

  – Context known by one party but not the other

  – Incorrect assumptions of shared understanding by both parties

  – A lack of *active listening* on the receiver's part (covered below)

Because there exists so much potential for disruption in communication, the sender needs to take responsibility for attempting to *confirm understanding*. By following up on the original message with a question or seeking nonverbal cues, the chance of a mismatch between what was sent and what was received is decreased. When an indication of misunderstanding is perceived, the sender should stop, take actions to clarify and confirm understanding, and then continue in a way that attempts to minimize the difficulties just experienced.

Active Listening

Most of the concepts covered in this chapter are directly applicable to the sender and the way they "encode" a message, but by *actively listening*,[3] the receiver can also improve the communication process. Active listening is a structured and intentional process. After carefully listening and fully hearing what the sender is saying, the receiver takes responsibility for affirming their understanding of what was said by asking for clarification or further details as needed.

This back-and-forth between sender and receiver is known as *interactive communication*. The defining feature of interactive communication is the ability for the sender and receiver to affect each other as communication is happening. This can be as simple as the sender watching for signs of confusion while speaking to the receiver. The ability of both parties to interact can be affected quite significantly by the channel or combination of channels chosen. Modern times have brought new paradigms of interactivity—while email is primarily one-way-at-a-time, newer, more instant messaging platforms can bring instant feedback or even allow for more direct interaction as needed. Consider, for example, how messaging through a smartphone often includes the easily-selectable option to initiate a voice or video communication if one party feels that it would enhance the conversation.

But what about scenarios where interactive communication isn't possible or practical? What if communication can only be one-way, such as a manager addressing a large group of stakeholders? In this scenario, several other types of communication may become necessary. These include *push communication, pull communication,* and *hybrid communication.*

5.3 Push/Pull Communication: A Hybrid Approach

One-way communication is generally divided into two categories.[4] *Push Communication* is delivered by the sender to one or more recipients; because of its nature, the sender can confirm it has been sent but cannot confirm receipt or understanding. A common example of push communication would be a public radio broadcast. *Pull Communication* is in some ways the opposite; the sender provides access to the message, and one or more recipients have the option of receiving it when they determine the need. An example of this would be a bulletin board on an office wall.

Push / Pull / Interactive Communication
Look again at the list of channels on page 152. On a piece of paper, copy each channel and, for each, place a right arrow ($\rightarrow$) to indicate that it is primarily push communication, a left arrow ($\leftarrow$) to indicate pull communication, and a double-sided arrow ($\leftrightarrow$) to indicate interactive communication. Are each of these clear-cut? Do some have multiple interpretations?

Because push and pull communication are fundamentally different, each presents distinct benefits and ideal uses. The primary weakness is generally the same for both: confirmation of receipt or understanding are difficult to ascertain.

- **Push Communication**

    - Primary Strength: The sender knows when and to whom it was directed.
    - Ideal Uses: Non-urgent communication or information not requiring immediate response.

- **Pull Communication**

  - Primary Strength: Access is at the receiver's discretion, which helps to avoid "information overload."

  - Ideal Uses: Non-vital communications or information that needs to be accessed frequently by multiple parties.

In situations where the benefits of interactive communication are unavailable and the sender must choose push or pull communication, adopting a *hybrid* approach often provides the optimal solution. Consider the following scenario:

> Having managed the project for three months, Jamie has generally approached resources and stakeholders face-to-face, knowing that interactive communication is preferable. Recently, absenteeism and the greater reach of the project to some of the company's international offices have required choices to be made regarding whether to use push or pull communication.
>
> Because of the size and complexity of the project, many older documents have been stored in a server-based repository. This has been especially useful to Jamie when a new team member needs to be brought up to speed: the process is as simple as attaching one or more of these archived documents to an email and sending it on its way—it travels around the globe in an instant!
>
> Through various types of communication and careful archival of each vital project document, Jamie feels that the project has a reasonably good chance of meeting its deadline, though two major concerns have recently appeared: 1) because of this project's global reach, team members have expressed concern about proper access to documentation in other time zones, and 2) management has begun to ask about the security of the project, specifically relating to the documentation of some not-yet-patented ideas.

Should Jamie use *push* or *pull* communication? Remember, the *push* approach, which is currently being employed, involves attaching the needed document to an email and sending it to the recipient. This has several drawbacks:

- The ever-present "firehose of emails" can lead to "information overload," with recipients often unable to find what they need later on.

- If a recipient forwards the email (attachment included) to a third party, security may be compromised.

- Documents that are currently in the process of creation by more than one team member must be emailed back-and-forth leading to "versioning hell."

- All of these attachments can lead to over-capacity inboxes, requiring emails and attachments to be deleted, leading to potential data loss (at least historical data).

Instead of downloading and attaching, Jamie could choose a *pull* approach. When a new piece of documentation is added to the project, appropriate team members already have secure access to the server location. In this manner, they can simply download what they need when they need it. However, this also has drawbacks:

- How will recipients to know which documents are more important than others? Or which are appropriate for the work and decisions currently important to the project? Context may not be readily available.

- In some cases, email (or push communication) is a stakeholder's preferred medium of exchange. Is it wise to force this type of change?

- Without the "push" action of the email, it's possible that the project could be more easily ignored or perceived as being a lower priority.

A third option, a *hybrid communication* approach, can solve many of the issues listed above. The key to making this work lies in the electronic document repository. What if, instead of attaching the document to an email, Jamie sent a *link* to the document in the repository? This turns many of the drawbacks into benefits:

- Because an email (push) is still sent, Jamie is still given the opportunity to provide context to the document being linked. Because no attachments are included, the email size is minimized, and so is the chance of deletion due to limits on inbox storage capacity.

- The repository server most likely offers user authentication. This requires some more planning on Jamie's part in terms of access control, but vastly increases security. If an email is forwarded inappropriately, the outsider cannot access the document. Stakeholders requesting access can be given either read-only or editing ability as needed—the team may have overlooked them in the first place, and now they can be added to appropriate communications. Because many repositories are tied to a corporate authentication system, termination of an employee will often simultaneously revoke their access to these documents.

- Documents can be readily changed without requiring a new email. If an error is found within the document after the communication, recipients following the included link see the new version automatically.

- Versioning is often included in repositories—this means that the historical context (old versions) of the document can be retained and accessed if needed.

- Related to the last benefit, if more than one team member wishes to revise a document, the server, rather than email, becomes the medium of exchange.

- This structure is extremely friendly to those who prefer pull communication (and a global, time-shifted project team)—the documentation is there when they are ready to use it.

- Many repositories offer search capabilities that allow you to search within documents, greatly decreasing the time it takes to find a particular piece of information.

- Documents can *live* in new ways. A meeting agenda, for instance, can be expanded to include meeting minutes during or after the meeting occurs. Now any email related the meeting includes access to the whole of its documentation, regardless of when it is accessed. Putting all of these agendas in one repository "folder" gives them a home and context with each other.

- The emails themselves can be archived there as well, receiving the benefits listed above as well as allowing future projects or new team members to learn from them.

Though this approach carries many benefits, this solution is still not appropriate for every situation. As the project leader, Jamie needs to consider both the needs of the receivers and of the project when deciding how to communicate. In some cases, this will require fully interactive communication. The following section, covering meeting success, provides some guidelines for group-based interactive communication.

5.4 Communications within the Team: Meeting Success

There are few parts of corporate life that people seem to dread more than meetings. Is *every* meeting "dread-worthy"? Have you ever had a "good" meeting? If so, what was the subject of the meeting? Regular meeting attendees often share the same types of complaints:

- **"My time could be better spent:"** The information shared in the meeting could have been shared more efficiently or the meeting was simply too long.

- **"Most of what was discussed wasn't relevant to me:"** In many cases, other people were talking amongst themselves and the topic of conversation didn't affect all parties.

- **"It felt disorganized:"** This could speak to a lack of time management, who should speak when, a key person gone missing, or a lack of planning beforehand.

The harsh reality is this: most meetings shouldn't occur in the first place. This is the result of several common mistakes:

- **Discussion or debate is out of control:** If debate is important, then it's also important to set and enforce guidelines around that debate. This means that a facilitator (who should act as a neutral party) sets and enforces strict time and attendance guidelines as well as a set of ground rules for the discussion. If possible, this type of meeting should be separate from regularly scheduled meetings, and decisions/results should be recorded and published to avoid rehashing old arguments.

- **Attendees are unprepared:** The unfortunate truth is that some people see meetings as a pretense for work; these people prefer discussion, debate, and meetings to individual actions and contributions because they are easier or require less individual accountability. By showing up to multiple meetings (even unprepared), they are lulled into feeling a false sense of contribution. Although what's described here isn't always the case, it's important to place value on *each* attendee's time. Whenever possible, the meeting coordinator or project leader should confirm that key attendees are prepared; if not, the meeting should be canceled or rescheduled to better suit the needs of its attendees.

- **The facilitator isn't prepared:** This takes the previous mistake to the next level. A properly prepared facilitator has created and distributed a unique agenda (no "standing agendas"), arrives early to ensure that facilities and technology are set, and has the authority and organizational skills needed to keep the discussion on-task. Especially dangerous can be "standing meetings," or meetings that occur at the same time each week—these types of arrangements work best if the facilitator is prepared to cancel when nothing of vital importance is on the agenda (be sure not to confuse "standing meetings" with "stand-up meetings," discussed in *Agile Status Meetings* on the next page).

- **Circumstances weren't properly considered:** Sometimes a meeting is doomed before it starts. Reasons could include:

  - **Bad timing:** Too early or late in the day, workweek, month, or quarter. Is a Friday 4:30 meeting optimal?

  - **The wrong attendees:** Too many is a common issue. People's time is valuable and should be respected and optimized.

  - **Distractions:** Are other events happening in close proximity? Is the meeting space appropriate?

  - **Interpersonal issues:** Sometimes the people in the meeting are the reason for its failure. For some examples and resolutions, see *Managing Conflict* on page 126 and *Team Pitfalls* on page 180.

This last common mistake is the most surprising to many:

- **It's a subject not appropriate for a meeting:** The most common offender here is the "status meeting," in which each party discusses their accomplishments and how their progress pertains to the project. This purpose is much better served by the project leader, who can hold individual discussions with each team member, collate their statuses, measure them against the plan, and send out a communication with the results. That being said, what are some good reasons to hold a meeting? Strategic planning and communication, risk management, group educational/teambuilding experiences, and recognition of achievements are all examples of great reasons to hold a meeting (see *Risk Management* on page 97, *Building Trust* on page 125, and *Motivators* on page 7).

Agile Status Meetings

Are status meetings a "necessary evil"? Agile methods, discussed in the appendix, often address this type of meeting with strict limits— According to Mike Cohn, the "Daily Scrum" (a.k.a. the "Daily Stand-Up Meeting"), for instance, often requires attendees to physically stand (when practical), limits preparation time to 5 minutes, and limits meeting time to 10-15 minutes total.[5] See page 205 for more on *Daily Stand-Up Meetings*, and page 202 for other types of Agile meetings.

Given how many pitfalls are present, how can a project leader ever hope to hold a successful meeting? By following these rules, their chance for success is maximized:

1. **Manage time properly:** This applies to both the meeting itself and before the meeting is held. Good advanced notice is needed to avoid unprepared attendees, and strict pacesetting and curation of the meeting ensure that each topic receives an appropriate amount of attention. Another element of time management is the frequency in which the meeting is held. Does the meeting cycle match the pace of the project or team it serves?

2. **Prepare beforehand:** Though this seems obvious, complacency can cause even the most dedicated leaders to become lax in thinking about the meeting's purpose, preparing and sending agendas, and "doing their homework" (checking in with key attendees and preparing subject material for reference and discussion). A proper agenda should include the following:

   - Attendee names and roles; meeting location, date, and time
   - Meeting roles such as the facilitator, timekeeper, and scribe
   - Technology to be implemented, such as a call-in information, screen-sharing, two-way video, and presentation slides
   - A meeting objective statement
   - A schedule for the meeting itself: discussion topics, etc.
   - Information about where the agenda and follow-up items are archived

Sample Agendas

Numerous examples of meeting agendas are available online or via templates built into most word processors—but is it possible that your organization already has one? Many companies, especially those who have received ISO 9001 certification, already have an agenda format available. Try searching your organization's resources or asking other project leaders.

3. **Document and follow-up:** Many make the mistake of thinking the meeting ends when everyone walks out of the room. For the facilitator, a good portion of their work remains—the minutes, results, action items, and deliverables should have been recorded for distribution afterward. Decisions made, artifacts, and other output need to be properly stored, updated, and disseminated. Action items and deliverables need to be appropriately assigned, preferably with clear time limits and information about who should be notified when they are completed.

What to do with Meeting Documentation

So you've followed all of the advice above, but what to do with all of these artifacts? Why not use the *Hybrid Push/Pull Approach* discussed on page 155? By using a single document for both the agenda and post-meeting documentation, you are easing access for anyone seeking information about what took place.

Will the team still hate meetings? It's possible! But by seeking to avoid the pitfalls and following the steps listed above, a project leader or meeting facilitator can begin to reap the benefits that meetings offer—and productive meetings will eventually become engrained in (and expected from) the team's overall culture.

5.5   Ethics in Communication

In projects, ethics are more intertwined with communication than any other area—what we say, what we choose not to say, and how we say it present a continuous challenge to both project leaders and individual team members. Although there are ethical considerations outside of communication, most of these are a binary decision that needs to be made at one point in time: "Am I OK with working for a tobacco company?", for instance. Communication-related ethics are an ongoing stream of decisions, each of which require ethical consideration. The majority of project-related ethics relate to continuously seeking and communicating the truth. Some guidelines include:[6]

- **Honesty before the project begins:** Truthfulness starts when considering whether or not to engage a project. Were early estimates given proper consideration? When creating the contract, did all parties negotiate in good faith? The tone that is set at this early stage will resonate throughout the rest of the project.

- **Trying to understand the truth:** When in pursuit of the truth, we need to remember that sometimes our perception of truth may not be accurate. If this possibility is brought to light, it becomes the project leader's (and team's) responsibility to seek the whole truth, even if this brings new difficulties into the project (for an example, see *Blowhard Jamboree* on page 180).

- **Being truthful in all communications:** Though this may seem obvious, it can really be put to the test when the project is in trouble. Even the most well-intentioned project leader may at times be tempted to report that the project is on track, fully intending to catch up later. What many don't realize is that the ability to accurately communicate and work through bad news often serves to strengthen bonds of trust both with stakeholders and within the team. As such, it is essential that you navigate the dynamics incumbent in accurate communication and be willing to share bad news whenever it becomes a reality (see *Building Trust* on page 125).

- **Creating an environment where others tell the truth:** Truthfulness should be a part of the team's culture. By consistently telling the truth as a leader or team member, you consistently communicate that only the truth is acceptable. When falsehoods are discovered, team members should feel positive "peer pressure" to resolve mistruths and communicate honestly (see *Matching Leadership with Culture* on page 10).

Each of these influences the team dynamic as well as its outward relation with stakeholders. Ethical consideration happens primarily at the individual level—we must each decide to act in an ethical manner, or, if we see others acting unethically, we must decide whether or how to respond. This personal discipline is discussed in chapter 1 (see *Professional Discipline and Ethics* on page 15).

Though many ethical considerations are related to inwardly-facing communications, communications with stakeholders most often present the opportunities that tempt us to violate ethical standards. Metrics and reports, numbers, especially the way we present them, are often quite easy to manipulate for personal benefit. As you read the next section, consider the ethical implications of the factors and examples discussed.

5.6   Communicating with Metrics and Reports

Let's face it—though they seem straightforward, the reality of numbers is that they are easily manipulated and at times difficult to draw real value from. In many cases, project leaders are interested in statistics' usefulness but hesitant to communicate actual numbers because of the potential for negative interpretation. Questions begin to present themselves: Are these numbers *actually* useful? Do they cast an inaccurate view of the project? Are we in danger of a draconian "management by the numbers" scenario?

The statistics of projects are generally called *metrics*. The following may seem a wide generalization, but nonetheless we must state it: metrics are only important if they help the project team make important decisions. They generally provide some sort of context required for the proper consideration of available choices. Metrics can generally be divided into two types:

- **Private Metrics:** Generally known only to the project team and are important to their everyday self-optimization. A common example would be "Errors Found per Week." The value outside of the team is limited and disclosure would in many cases result in misinterpretation or undue concern.

- **Public Metrics:** More formal and meant to be disseminated outside of the core team. A common example would be "Schedule Variance," or how far off schedule the project is. These metrics are valuable to a wider set of stakeholders and are generally more direct in their interpretation.

Private metrics are often the subject of daily one-on-one conversations or team-only meetings—in some cases, these metrics may be "rolled-up" into more generally-applicable public metrics. Public metrics also are an important element of project communication, but like statistics, they have a potential for misunderstanding, manipulation, and wasted effort.

Reports, in large part, are collections of metrics that add trending information, context, and organization. Though reports vary somewhat from individual metrics, their core principles are similar, and they share many of the same potential downsides.

So how do we make metrics and reports useful? By properly collecting, analyzing, packaging, and communicating them to stakeholders. When sending metrics and reports, consider the following:

- **Level of detail:** This is surprisingly hard to get right. Some prefer to send all of the data down to the most intricate detail. Others roll everything up, only sending one number. Success lies in the balance—and knowing what each stakeholder prefers.

- **The communication channel:** Like the level of detail, this can vary. A spreadsheet is better prepared to handle detailed statistics than a typed-out email is. In some cases, the communication channel and level of detail can work together, by including, for example, a summary in an email with a link to more detailed numbers (a *hybrid* approach, covered on page 157).

- **The role and wishes of the recipient:** A project leader needs to consider who is to receive the information. A direct manager probably has more time and interest to devote to detailed numbers than a C-level executive. In some cases, recipients at the same level may also have different wishes—the easiest way to know? Just ask.

- **What the recipient is to use the information for:** Are the reports to be read by human eyes, or are they to be rolled up into another report that the recipient is creating? In some cases, project leaders have spent hours pulling and formatting numbers from a spreadsheet only to have a recipient spend hours moving the data into their own spreadsheet—both parties unaware of the other. Once again, ask what the recipient is using the data for.

- **Interpretation:** It is not inappropriate to provide some enhancements to your numbers, such as a baseline or trend information, extrapolation, or interpretation. This can be extremely helpful to someone who isn't as connected to the project as the sender. This is also a potential area where obfuscation or "positive spin" may be inappropriately added—be careful! (an ethical consideration, covered in the previous section.)

Now that we know how to make them useful, what are some common metrics and reports?

Example Project Metrics

Metrics are often a single number or ratio. Remember to give proper, ethical context when sharing them with stakeholders.

Cycletime

Cycletime is the average period of time required to complete one cycle. The definition of a single cycle can vary, from the entire project to how long a single phase

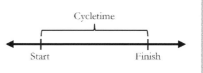

takes. This is used for schedule-oriented comparison.

Schedule or Cost Variance

Variance is a reference to how far the actual earned value (see *Project Tracking* on page 94) is from the expected/ committed schedule or budget (called a

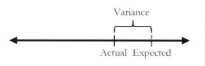

baseline) at the current point in time. This is useful for extrapolating whether the committed end date or budget will be met. A related metric would simply be the percent complete or actual Earned Value.

Resource Utilization

Resource Utilization typically tracks the utilization of the team (human resources), though there are similar metrics for non-human resources. It's calculated as the percentage of available resource hours currently being charged to the project in a given period (such as a week). A number significantly below 100% means that resources are possibly being

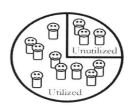

wasted; over 100% means overtime or potential burnout—both speak to the possibility of inefficiency.

Requirements Volatility

Requirements or specifications changes are extremely taxing on traditional plan-focused projects (see page 37), which prefer that all requirements are fixed before proceeding. Requirement Volatil-

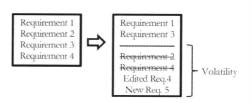

ity is the number of new, changed, or dropped requirements or specifications divided by the original number of requirements or specifications.

Total Risk Exposure

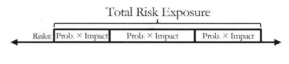

Typically expressed in time or money, Total Risk Exposure is the sum of all individual risk exposures. As the project progresses, this number is expected to peak and eventually decrease as risks occur or the time when they would have occurred passes (see *Risk Management* on page 97).

Customer Satisfaction

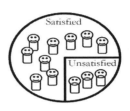

Considered by some to be the most important metric, Customer Satisfaction can be measured in several different ways, most commonly through a quantitative survey given at consistent time intervals. Though measuring is relatively easy, deducing the reasons why changes in customer satisfaction have occurred is much harder.

It should be noted that the metrics listed above are general in nature. In many cases specific organizations or industries will have their own sets of metrics. Examples include "Design Complexity" metrics used in mechanical engineering and "Code Defect Density" metrics in software engineering.

Example Project Reports

Project reports are much more comprehensive than metrics; care must be taken not to include *too much* information, which may serve to obfuscate important information.

Status Report

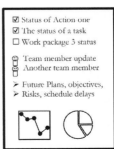

Because this report is so commonly used, its format can vary widely from project-to-project. Some organizations even have a published, preferred format. At minimum, a Status Report will usually include the following sections:

- **Overall health:** Including accomplishments, completed tasks, and metrics such as Customer Satisfaction.
- **Schedule and budget status:** A realistic view of the expended time and money vs. the schedule and budget.

- **Issues:** Typically expressed as current problems, a proactive project also lists *potential* issues (*risks*, covered on page 97, for example).

Notes: One example Status Report is this chapter's tool: the Quad Chart (page 173). As discussed earlier in the chapter, sharing status is by itself a poor reason for a meeting: the Status Report can replace the less-preferred "Status Meeting" (see *Team Meeting Success* on page 159).

Metrics/Data to Include: Milestones Complete, current actions, planned actions, Schedule Variance, Cost Variance, issues, risks, Total Risk Exposure, major changes (associated with Requirements Volatility), clarification/analysis/interpretation where needed.

Trend/Forecasting Report

Looking back is important for extrapolating into the future. This type of report interprets data from the project, combines it with other data (including from other projects), attempts to determine if performance is improving/deteriorating, and/or forecasts into the upcoming time period. Elements may include:

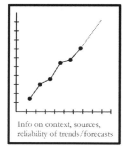

Info on context, sources, reliability of trends/forecasts

- **Schedule, budget, or deliverables:** The report may focus on one or many elements of the project—where it's been and where it seems to be heading.
- **Charts or graphs:** The goal here should be to allow easier interpretation of the data—be sure that the way the data is presented does not obfuscate the truth behind the numbers.
- **Analysis and statistical information:** When forecasting, it's important to include justifications and ranges of probability.

Notes: It may be possible to generate these types of reports automatically, providing up-to-date data whenever needed and reducing opportunities for adding bias.

Metrics/Data to Include: Cycletime, schedule, and cost data, Utilization, or anything else trending/in need of forecasting.

Variance Report

Variance Reports measure how actual results compare to baselines, or "how far from the expected" the numbers are. It is important to understand that although time flows at a consistent rate, the rate at which a project is expected to complete work or spend capital varies according to the plan that has been laid out. *Underspending* can be just as serious as *overspending* as a project proceeds. Just as a doctor might compare a developing child to expected height and weight figures, variance

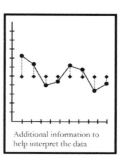

Additional information to help interpret the data

reports attempt to gauge the health of the project by comparing its progress to expected values.

Notes: Variance Reports typically employ tables and graphs—proactive project leaders include trend or forecasting information as well.

Metrics/Data to Include: Schedule Variance, Cost Variance, clarification/analysis/interpretation where needed.

Earned Value Report

Although this report includes similar information to the reports listed above, the Earned Value Report follows a more specific method. (The basis of this is covered in the *Project Tracking* section on page 94.) What it tries to ascertain is where the project is in "pure" Earned Value/cost management terms. Scrum's Daily Burndown Chart (see page 201) shares many features with the Earned Value Report.

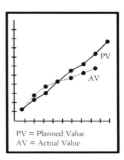

PV = Planned Value
AV = Actual Value

Notes: The data is almost always expressed on a line-graph, which plots "Planned Value" and "Earned Value" against each other. Ideally, the two lines would match perfectly—space between the two indicates a project that is ahead of or behind schedule (Variance).

Metrics/Data to Include: Earned Value, Planned Value.

Lessons Learned

While many of the other reports are based largely on quantitative data and facts, this report focuses more on the qualitative side of work and the opinions influencing the project. Throughout the project, both the project leader and the team should be continuously asking, and answering, the question: "What information could be useful for future projects?" By sharing Lessons Learned beyond the team, the organization at large has the opportunity to benefit.

> Future projects & teams:
>
> Start doing these things:
> ☑ Meeting agendas
> ☑ Analyze stakeholders
> Stop doing these things:
> ☹ Uncontrolled conflict
> ☹ Violating team trust
> Continue doing these things:
> ☺ Culture of respect
> ☺ Tracking progress
> What went well: ...
> What went poorly: ...

Notes: The Lessons Learned effort at the close of a project is often called a postmortem. Given the morbidity of this name, remember that lessons from successful projects are just as if not more important than those from failed projects. Agile's principle of regular self-reflection (covered on page 215) prioritizes Lessons Learned.

Metrics/Data to Include: Project artifacts (documents), analysis, Risks Anticipated/Occurred, Customer Satisfaction data, milestones and metrics collected throughout the project.

When using metrics and reports, and especially when communicating them to stakeholders, it's important to remember two things:

1. In order to have the benefits of statistically valid metrics, the team must be careful to consistently and accurately collect the data, and

2. The way to make reports and metrics useful is by viewing them from the stakeholder's perspective. Adding a small amount of analysis or clarity can have a huge effect on their value.

Taking the time to view things from the stakeholders' perspective is a key success factor in *stakeholder expectation management*, discussed in the next section.

5.7 Stakeholder Expectation Management

According to a recent CHAOS Research Report by The Standish Group, 39% of projects are fully successful, 43% are late/over budget/missing deliverables, and 18% fail alltogether.[7] With almost two-thirds of projects failing to meet expectations, the whole idea of project communication has a very real problem on its hands.

Given that so many projects are "under-delivering," would a better strategy be to "under-promise and over-deliver"? At first blush this may seem like the answer, but this approach neglects the way projects typically operate. Projects are created to provide a return on investment (ROI) to the organization initiating them; if this anticipated return is undercut (i.e. "under promised"), then the very real danger exists of the project never starting in the first place.

So how do we manage this quandary? For the project itself, many of the practices involved here have already been discussed in chapters 3 and 4; concepts such as proper estimating, understanding commitment, consistent tracking, and risk management are vital. Although the project itself may be properly managed, have you ever considered how to strike the proper balance when communicating with stakeholders?

As defined in chapter 1, stakeholders are "people who can affect or are affected by the execution or outcome of a project." According to this definition, both of these groups need communication:

- **Stakeholders affecting the project:** Because they have so much influence, this stakeholder group often *demands* the most attention. Meeting that demand is wise, as they often can and do cause the most disruption to a project. Not anticipating the expectations of individuals in this group represents a major risk to the project (see *Risk Management* on page 97).

- **Stakeholders who are affected by the project:** Although it's easy to focus on those stakeholders who have the potential to thoroughly disrupt our project, it's of vital importance not to forget those who are the most affected by our actions. Because these people in many cases don't have the ability to directly intervene or disrupt a project, it's up to the project leader and team to properly *advocate* for them.

Both of these groups are expected to care about project objectives and the end product, but there are other project elements that may also be of concern to them. Most often, these groups seek *information* in the form of progress and expectation updates. Chapter 2's discussion of the attributes of quality includes an element which has communication at its core: *perception* (see page 45). While analyzing who these stakeholders are, the project team should try to anticipate each stakeholder's expectations, planning to meet them with a proper response—not doing so risks disappointment or even project failure. Consider the following when managing expectations:

- **Expectations are affected by stakeholders' own experiences and biases:** This means, for example, that a previous project, one you weren't even involved with, might have a negative effect on your stakeholder's perception of your project.

- **Expectations follow a pattern—stakeholders are often creatures of habit:** If you have done something every Tuesday for the last two months, it's reasonable for others to expect that pattern to continue.

- **Sometimes all you need to do is ask:** Though there may occasionally be difficulties beyond this, often all that is needed is to ask each stakeholder about their expectations.

- **Expectations are based on what you've said before:** This may seem obvious, but it's surprising how often a project leader can become frustrated with a stakeholder's demands even though they exactly match what was originally promised.

- **Hard data can be extremely valuable:** Metrics and reports are a valuable asset in setting and managing expectations, especially with stakeholders who prefer to analyze the data themselves (covered in the last section).

How, then, are expectations actively managed? In most cases, this comes down to regular communication: anticipating what the receiver might expect, developing a strategy with this in mind, and executing that strategy of regular communication. If possible, these communications should be customized based on the individual profiles of the project's stakeholders. Further insight into stakeholders' relationship with the project, including insight into how to prioritize them, is covered in chapter 3 on page 102.

Documenting Your Communication Plan
Wondering how to document your specific project communication requirements? The *Stakeholder Communication Plan* is an important artifact of any project and contains specifics such as what, how, when, and who. A listing of specific components is articulated on page 67.

5.8 Chapter Tool: The Quad Chart

One problem that project managers commonly experience is deciding exactly how to communicate status effectively to management, customers, and other stakeholders; it's often tough to balance level of detail, what to and what not to include, and consistency.

The Quad Chart, also known as the 4-Up, is a relative of the executive summary in that it is required to fit on one presentation slide or one side of a piece of paper. This page is divided into four equal panels, with each forcing prioritization of its contents due to limitations in space. In addition to a header (with the project name and contact info) these 4 panels are typically used to denote *Progress*, *Plans*, *Risks*, and *Decisions/Resources Needed*. Usually updated weekly, the Quad Chart is a good complement to the meeting agenda, allowing stakeholders to quickly ascertain status from its consistent and straightforward format.

The following is a brief example relating to a software project:

Accomplished Tasks: Week 4	**Planned Tasks: Week 5**
✓ Project Plan first draft (Drew) 　✓ Change control board 　✓ Release schedule ✓ Use case modeling (Joe) ✓ Create reporting folders/ 　spreadsheets (Mary) ✓ Basic risk management (Drew) ✓ High priority Use Cases (All)	• Medium level Use Cases (Joe) • Refine high-level Use Cases 　(Mary) • Refactor feature list (Steve) • Architecture notebook (Drew) • Upload all metrics (Steve) • Requirements spreadsheet (Mary)
Ongoing Risks (bold indicates new or changed risks) • Team does not have adequate resources to reliably develop for mobile environment • **Time spent on Use Cases** • No team member has gone through a whole project using the new process before	**Needs/Discussions: Week 5** • Department: 　– Mobile developer account 　– Access to shared mobile 　　developer environment • Customer: 　– Review Use Cases offline

In many ways, the Quad Chart is the ultimate exercise in prioritization (the subject of chapter 3). Thinking about what was done, what need to be done, and any associated risks and needs often leads to long, unfocused lists; when you are forced to comply with the one-page requirement, however, you must decide on what's more pertinent or immediate to your communication. By focusing on communicating only the most vital items, you can comply with the "80-20 principle" (also known as the Pareto principle[8]), which suggests that 80 percent of the problems come from 20 percent of the project.

Your Project's Quad Chart
Using the template below, create a Quad Chart for a project you are leading or participating in. Before you begin, think about who might receive it regularly, what they would prefer to see, and what needs to be communicated. When completing each panel, think about what information has the highest priority and eliminate less important items as you fill it out.

Project Name:	Date:
Accomplished Tasks:	**Planned Tasks:**
Ongoing Risks:	**Needs/Discussions:**

5.9   Summary and Conclusion

Because communication is such a large part of our lives, it is easy to forget that (like every other part of a project) there are methods, practices, and guidelines to follow. Both the sender and receiver must consider the channel of communication as well as potential blockers such as their own attitudes towards the other person. It is especially important for the project leader to think about how they conduct their communications. When interactive communication isn't available, they must carefully consider whether *push*, *pull*, or *hybrid* communication is most appropriate.

Team meetings represent a large responsibility for many leaders—preparing properly, ensuring all important parties are present, and carefully monitoring the agenda are all vital to achieving success. Communications external to the team are equally important; the team must consider which information is appropriate for which stakeholder groups, what metrics or reports could enhance their message, and whether the form and frequency of communication is preferred by those stakeholders.

What's more, the thread underlying all these decisions is a productive and continuous consideration of ethics. Seeking honesty, telling the truth, and creating an environment where others are also encouraged to do so represent a proactive approach: in the field of ethics, deciding to do the right thing *ahead of time* is key. Honestly communicating difficult news to an important stakeholder is not only important for the project, but is also an important element of building trusting, long-term relationships with them.

By considering *who* we are communicating with, *what* to say, *how* to say it, and *how frequently* to say it, a good portion of project communication becomes a matter of planning and execution. In this planning and execution cycle, there are many variables, but the most important action any team can take is to place a high priority on planning their communication strategy *ahead of time*—considering the needs of others and really listening to their stakeholders.

When communicating, a team will inevitably make mistakes from time-to-time. Have you noticed, however, that there are some mistakes that seem to follow an often-repeated pattern? In the next chapter, we grapple with some common pitfalls project teams experience, and we address how to avoid them.

Key Terms

Active Listening: An intentionally structured method in which the *receiver* takes responsibility for successful communication by affirming understanding (page 154).

Communication Blocker: A disruption to the meaning or perception of a communication. This can be the result of an issue within the *communication channel* or with the *sender* or *receiver* (page 153).

Communication Channel: The path through which communication must travel, also known as a "medium" (page 151).

Hybrid Communication: A communication method which combines *push* and *pull communication*. Messages containing links to persistent "pullable" artifacts are "pushed" (page 157).

Interactive Communication: Dynamic, two(or more)-way communication characterized by the *sender* and *receiver's* ability to affect each other throughout (page 154).

Metric: A useful, quantitative value or combination of measurements which allows the team or stakeholders to assess a project attribute, assisting decision-making processes. Often a component of *reports* (page 164).

Pull Communication: A message which allows *receivers* to retrieve the communication when they prefer, but doesn't allow for confirmation of receipt or understanding. Websites are a common example (page 155).

Push Communication: A message delivered from the *sender* to one or more recipients without the ability to confirm that they've received or understood the communication. Postal mail is a common example (page 155).

Quad Chart: A regularly updated and published one-page project summary consisting of four panels denoting information such as progress, plans, needs, and *risks* (page 173).

Sender: In communications, the party who is conveying the message, typically with particular *receiver(s)* in mind (page 153).

Receiver: In communications, the party to whom the message is being conveyed by the *sender* (page 153).

Report: A project artifact, often communicated to stakeholders, which allows its recipient to gain understanding of an aspect of the project. Often contains *metrics* (page 164).

Review Questions

1. A team of 3 adds one additional member. How many communication channels does this add?

2. A colleague's tone of voice implies that he doesn't fully agree with what he is saying. What communication types are illustrated here?

3. Is active listening an example of push, pull, interactive, or hybrid communication?

4. A key attendee at an important meeting has stated that they won't be able to prepare beforehand. What should the facilitator do?

5. Which single concept is most important in communicating ethically?

6. Of the two types of metrics, which is visible to the most stakeholders?

7. Which metric is defined by how far the actual earned value is from the expected/committed value?

8. Three quarters of the way through a project, the customer wants to know what the total cost may be. Which report is appropriate?

Exercises

1. A team member has recently been delivering work late, in some cases causing the team to miss important deadlines. As team leader, you've decided that it may be appropriate to use both formal and informal communication to address this issue. How would you implement this strategy?

2. Your team has been experiencing some communication difficulties since adding three additional team members who reside and work in another part of the world. What are some obvious and less obvious communication blockers that could be affecting the team? Be sure to include examples of how this may play out.

3. You are planning a large product launch event; invitees will include your team, management, and your external customer. Pertaining to the venue, invitations, schedule, and presentations at the event, describe a separate scenario when each of interactive, push, pull, and hybrid communication methods would be most appropriate.

4. You know that many of your team considers your meetings to be "painful," as one member put it. You suspect length is a major factor in this widespread

dissatisfaction. Describe three basic strategies you could take to shorten your
meetings while still accomplishing what they've set out to do.

5. The team to which you've just been assigned to lead seems to "bend the truth"
quite often, especially when communicating with the customer—you can understand why, as you yourself are tempted to do so at times. What are some steps
you could take personally and with the team to correct the situation?

6. It seems like every time you've given an estimate in the past, your actual time-
to-delivery has been longer than your prediction. You're considering "padding,"
or adding to your next estimate to keep this from happening. Is this a good or
bad idea? What are the potential consequences of doing so? Are there ethical
implications associated with this decision?

7. Review the *project triangle* on page 46. For each metric listed starting on page
166, which side or sides of the triangle are "targeted"?

Notes

[1]Shannon, C. E. and Weaver, W. *The mathematical theory of communication*. Urbana, Illinois:
University of Illinois Press. 1949.

[2]Appelo, Jurgen. *The Optimal Team Size is Five.*
http://noop.nl/2009/04/the-optimal-team-size-is-five.html. 2009.

[3]Rogers, Carl R. and Farson, Richard E. *Active listening.* Chicago: Industrial Relations Center,
the University of Chicago. 1957.

[4]Project Management Institute. *A Guide to the Project Management Body of Knowledge – Fifth
Edition.* Project Management Institute Inc. p. 295. 2013.

[5]Cohn, Mike. *Daily Scrum Meeting.* Mountain Goat Software.
https://www.mountaingoatsoftware.com/agile/scrum/meetings/daily-scrum. Accessed December
2017.

[6]Though the considerations listed here are common to many codes of ethics, this list includes
elements from the Project Management Institute's 2006 *Code of Ethics and Professional Conduct.*

[7]The Standish Group International. *CHAOS Manifesto 2013.* 2013.

[8] Pareto, Vilfredo and Page, Alfred N. *Translation of Manuale di economia politica ("Manual of
political economy")*, A.M. Kelley. 1971.

Pitfalls to Identify and Avoid

In the conclusion of this book, we present an extensive list of common team and project issues with the hope that the reader can learn to regularly identify and avoid them.

As we suggested at the end of the previous chapter, some mistakes seem to be repeated over and over again in both teams and organizations. In his book, *Rapid Development*, Steve McConnell calls them "classic mistakes."[1] A catchy website might advertise "The 15 Biggest Mistakes Projects Make—Number 14 Will Shock You!"; others call them *antipatterns*.[2] Whatever the name, there are certain pitfalls—negative situations and mistakes—that experienced project leaders see over and over.

Patterns and Antipatterns

A *pattern* is a generally accepted, reusable solution to a commonly occurring problem. For example, vehicular intersections provide several common problems, and traffic lights are a commonly accepted solution. *Antipatterns* are the antithesis of this: well-known, common problems which are also commonly caused by the organization experiencing them. The pitfalls in this chapter are antipatterns, and the practices used to prevent them (and their remedies) are patterns.

As you read the following pitfalls, consider the competencies you've learned in the previous chapters—could following their guidelines prevent the pitfalls from occurring? Each the following pitfalls includes a basic description (including why they are harmful) and a basic strategy for avoidance or remedy. They are separated into two main categories: social pitfalls and process/project pitfalls; they are then listed alphabetically, and related pitfalls or negative practices are also included for reference.

Related Concepts
Some of the "related" items listed with each of these pitfalls aren't explicitly explained—if you're not familiar with them, consider searching them on the internet to further familiarize yourself before reading on.

6.1   Team Pitfalls

Some mistakes are available to any group of people who, through plan or circumstance, are working together. The following pitfalls apply to the team's interaction with each other and those around them—their effects are felt both within the team and in the project they are working on:

Blamestorming

During a "blamestorm," team members spend an unproductive amount of time admiring the problem, describing how things got that way, and seeking to place blame and responsibility. This has a tone of inquisition and forces people to shelter rather than learn from mistakes.

- **The Fix:** Measure progress based on facts, not opinions. Focus on the most important issues first—and the actions needed to resolve them, rather than the blame. Create a culture where mistakes are learning opportunities, not points of weakness.
- **Related:** Scapegoating, Witch-hunt, Cover-Your-Rear Mentality

Blowhard Jamboree

In this pitfall, opinions, misinformation, or bias of (so-called) experts improperly influence important decisions.[3] Because these opinions or misinformation are often touted as facts, they can form a flawed basis for planning, estimating, and other important project decisions that carry repercussions down the line.

- **The Fix:** Be honest about why you have an opinion. If evidence to support that opinion is not immediately obvious, spend more time analyzing the problem and potential solutions. Avoid poor sources of misinformation by assigning or seeking subject matter experts (the *specialist* role, covered in chapter 4 on page 121) who are responsible for finding and sharing relevant, fact-based input.

- **Related:** Weasel Words, Confirmation Bias (a cognitive bias)

Weasel Words

Have you ever read or used the words "experts say..."? "it stands to reason that..."? How about advertising terms such as "award-winning"? Collectively, these are known as *weasel words* (also called "anonymous authority"). They attempt to lend credibility to a statement without requiring the speaker to specifically state what references they have. Because of their nature, these types of phrases should be avoided during debate; when used, those present should ask the speaker for more information or clarification on their position.

GroupThink

One of the more well-known pitfalls, groupthink happens when teams value harmony and conformity over diversity of thought.[4] This typically results in a less creative decision-making process and less opposing viewpoints, defeating one of the main benefits of making decisions as a group.

- **The Fix:** Conflict should not be viewed as negative (see *Managing Conflict* on page 126) and the leader should be replaced with a facilitator if possible to avoid undue influence. Other options include randomly dividing the group in half and separating for two concurrent sub-group discussions and assigning a "devil's advocate" each time a discussion is held.
- **Related:** Peer Pressure, Bandwagon Effect

Heroics

Some projects succeed in spite of poor planning, execution, and expectation management due to long hours, overtime, and neglectful singlemindedness. "Heroes," the team's most valuable members whose extraordinary effort lead to project "success," often feel overworked and under-appreciated, which may lead to their departure. Project leaders or team members who see the project schedule realistically are often seen as pessimists or "non-believers."

- **The Fix:** Because this practice seems to be a part of so many organizational cultures, modern methods such as Agile emphasize a "sustainable pace" (see page 214 for more on this). Remember that encouraging a "can-do" attitude can create an environment that suppresses accuracy in estimates and execution. Strive to build a culture that values good work/life balance.

- **Related:** Death March (page 184)

Intellectual Violence

This practice commonly plays out as one party understands a theory, technology, or buzzword uses this knowledge to intimidate or subjugate others in a public or meeting situation.[5] This can result in a closed and defensive culture where everyone becomes afraid of revealing inexperience or lack of understanding in an ever-escalating war of information. Keep in mind that this sometimes happens inadvertently.

- **The Fix:** The awareness that another party doesn't know something is a make-or-break moment—instead of intellectual violence, the same situation makes the perfect opportunity for mentorship between the two parties, and a potentially disastrous situation becomes an opportunity for personal and team growth.
- **Related:** Bullying

Loose Cannon

Delivering projects and working in the team environment often comes with tight deadlines, difficult work products, and a whole host of variously unpleasant conditions. Because of these conditions, a team member who constantly creates disruption can have a multiplicative effect on the rest of the team. Often putting politics before substance, these individuals can have a demotivating effect on the team and present a risk to the project.

- **The Fix:** Beyond obvious tactics like termination, this risk can often be mitigated by providing the loose cannon with a mentor or one-on-one time with the manager. If the resource is an expert or the quality of their work is valuable, physically transferring them or offering a work-from-home option could alleviate the situation.
- **Related:** People Skills, Nepotism, Seagull Management

Seagull Management

Similar to a loose cannon, seagull managers "fly in, make a lot of noise, dump on everyone, then fly out."[6] Have you ever encountered a manager like this? Did they negatively affect productivity? If not the "seagull," did the project leader "go to bat" for the team?

Poor Project Team/Stakeholder Relations

In some cases, stakeholders just won't "click" with the project team. This may be because of differences in personality (i.e. motivators, influencers, culture), the result of schedule pressure, or because of unrealistic expectations each group has on the other. The reality is that business is often conducted in ways that cause friction—negotiation, financial transactions, market forces, and priority are all potential "agitators" that contribute to this intense dynamic.

- **The Fix:** If friction is occurring with stakeholders, the simplest option may be to choose one person in either party through which to funnel all communication (the *externally-facing* role, covered on page 120). In stressful times, some grumbling is common and could even provide some stress relief, but this should remain internal to the team. Proper estimating, scheduling, tracking, and risk management activities will often alleviate or remove the largest stressors (see chapter 3).
- **Related:** "Us vs. Them" Mentality

Wishful Thinking

Wishful thinking may be the most common pitfall teams experience. Examples include insufficient planning, ignoring risks, creating overly optimistic schedules, asking for an extended deadline but offering to complete more work before that deadline (see *Regressive Renegotiation* on page 185), and assuming that contractors or external resources will always deliver quality work on time with little monitoring.

- **The Fix:** Don't confuse positive thinking or optimism with wishful thinking. Realistically consider future scenarios—if one or more elements of your plan require things to go "just right," you may be falling victim to wishful thinking. The only real cure for this is realistic planning/scheduling/tracking (see *Project Scheduling* on page 88) and risk management (see *Risk Management* on page 97).
- **Related:** Procrastination, Blind Optimism

6.2   Process and Product Pitfalls

In addition to problems that arise when individuals come together as a team, the act of initiating, planning, and executing project work contributes its own set of perils that need to be monitored for and addressed to ensure smooth operation. The following pitfalls mostly relate to the processes needed to effectively carry out a project:

Analysis Paralysis

Although many teams make the opposite mistake, analysis paralysis involves a reluctance to move out of the early planning stages of a project.[7] This may be caused by a fear of failure or accountability, micromanagement, or a problem that has no apparent solution. If a project spends too much time in these stages, it may experience schedule pressure at later stages or even "death by planning"—an overly complex plan that crushes project work with process.

- **The Fix:** If the problem seems unsolvable, prototyping may help. Otherwise, the team may benefit from an incremental process (see examples starting on page 38) and a willingness to learn from failure.
- **Related:** The Law of Triviality, Fear of Commitment, Design by Committee

The Law of Triviality
Have you ever found your team debating something that really doesn't matter? C. Northcote Parkinson's "Law of Triviality" observes that organizations often give disproportionate weight to trivial issues.[8] When making a decision, make sure the decision process is worth the time it takes—if it's not, move on.

Death March

Have you ever participated in a project you felt was destined to fail? "Death marches" are characterized by unattainable goals or deadlines, unsustainable workloads, and supervisors who seem out of touch with the project team.[9] This type of project environment can have a devastating effect on morale and team member retention—often "heroes" who commit to the project's completion choose to leave soon after it's finished in fear they will encounter a similar situation in the future.

- **The Fix:** Avoid committing to due dates before estimation and scheduling activities are concluded (see *Estimates vs. Commitments* on page 83). Another fix is to increase schedule and tracking visibility to management. Finally, if a death march does occur, you should make an effort to reward successful team members with an incentive that exceeds the price (time, emotional) they paid while working on the project.

- **Related:** Sunk Cost, Regressive Renegotiation

Regressive Renegotiation
Have you ever asked for more time, only to walk away with more time *and* more to do, leaving you just as far behind (or worse) than you were before?[10] To avoid this, only negotiate one side of the project triangle (schedule, resources, or scope, covered on page 46) at a time, leaving all parties with a clear view of the trade-offs.

Fire Drill

The early causes of a "fire drill" include uncertainty around requirements or design, a hesitation to begin, or another early-project delay. Later in the project cycle, a series of ambitious or unrealistic goals are set or priorities are shifted frequently resulting in constant chaos.[11] In some organizations, the constantly changing, reactive nature of fire drills is the norm. It should be noted that some team members prefer this chaos, because their mediocre work is less likely

to be noticed. At all costs, however, these situations are red flags that should not be ignored.

- **The Fix:** Short of changing the circumstances, "project leader sheltering" is the most readily available solution. In this model, progress is internally steadied and better planned; externally, the leader acts as a single liaison to management and most stakeholders, rationally prioritizing work for the team to mitigate the chaos experienced earlier in the project's life cycle (see chapter 3 for more on *prioritization*).
- **Related:** Micromanagement, Thrashing

Thrashing
Sometimes team members work hard and long but seem to accomplish very little—this is called *thrashing*. This can be expressed as repeated work, misprioritization of effort, low quality work, or burnt-out team

members. The cure for thrashing is process, especially the prioritization activities discussed in chapter 3. A productive leader plans and prioritizes work continuously while watching out for thrashing—as well as the other pitfalls covered in this chapter.

Ineffectively Adding Resources to the Team

Although many examples of this exist, the two most common are a lack of a proper training and integration procedure for new team members and the ineffective managing of contractors. In some cases, project leaders try adding people late in the project hoping to "catch up" on missed work only to find that integrating the new resources leaves the team further behind.[12]

- **The Fix:** Adding resources should be planned with the understanding of when they are needed, how much lead time is needed to "bring them up to speed," and how much management effort will be needed to utilize them effectively.
- **Related:** Brook's Law, Social Loafing

Social Loafing

Have you ever noticed that larger teams sometimes get less done than if individuals had worked separately? Studies on this phenomenon, known as *social loafing*,[13] show that the individual anonymity of working in a group allows individuals to exert less effort than if they worked by themselves. So how do you counter this effect? By choosing appropriate motivators (covered on page 7) and showing participants that their contribution really matters.

Rushing to Execution

Rushing to the execution phase of projects can become so commonplace that people may begin to accept the consequences of doing so as fact rather than circumstance. Examples of vital planning steps that are often shortchanged in this situation include receiving stakeholder approval on requirements/specifications, design iterations, estimation activities, and risk management. Failing to properly complete *upstream* activities like these can have a major effect on the final product's quality.

- **The Fix:** The obvious solution here is to properly consider important early-project activities; one strategy that may help is to adopt a process that rewards a commitment to these activities and has well-respected "gates" which require thoroughly completing each step before proceeding to the next. An acute awareness of *lessons learned* is also important here (see *Lessons Learned* on page 170).

- **Related:** Technical/Design Debt (described on page 46)

Scope Creep

Also known as "feature creep," scope creep involves the slow addition of new features or requirements/specifications as the project progresses, ultimately exerting a major, negative impact on the schedule or resources. It should be noted that scope creep is just as likely to come from the project team as from the customer.

I wish the project manager would stop calling the customer a "Scope Creep"

- **The Fix:** Strong "change management" activities, such as requiring signoff for scope changes, forces proper consideration of potential creep. Proper documentation can also be helpful, as in some cases parties may not actually know they are causing an expansion of scope.
- **Related:** Gold-Plating, Over-Engineering

Silver Bullet

In the same way that a silver bullet may be considered a quick and easy solution for werewolves, many teams make the mistake of thinking that a new tool, technology, or process will have magical effect on their projects.[14] This impression might come from wishful thinking or other projects that have seen (or advertised) success. As reality sets in, many projects find themselves behind schedule, their mistaken optimism turned to disappointment.

- **The Fix:** Just as potential problems are managed as risks, so should opportunities (see *The Opposite of Risks* on page 101). Like risks, opportunities aren't certainties and should be approached systematically and cautiously.
- **Related:** Bleeding-Edge Mentality, Early Adopters

Are Pitfalls Risks?

Pitfalls share all three of the features that define risks (uncertainty, loss, and manageability—see *Risk Management* on page 97)—but are they actually risks? The short answer is yes, but they are unlikely to appear on most risk registers. Because of their broad, universal nature, pitfalls are hard to quantify into the probability and impact calculations needed to analyze them. They are a risk that must be monitored by both the team and the team leader, and simply understanding the nature of each pitfall is often enough to promote resistance to their taking root.

6.3   Chapter Tool: Pitfall "Hot Spots"

Each of the pitfalls in this chapter represents a constant hazard to both the team and the project it's working on, but there are parts of the project that represent "hot-spots," or areas of increased likelihood where the pitfall may manifest itself. If pitfalls do occur, their negative results will inevitably manifest themselves later in the project when "the damage has already been done." Put another way, mistakes or circumstances have a *downstream* effect on a project—this means that project leaders must carefully consider *upstream* manifestations of pitfalls as the project progresses and work to mitigate their effects down the road.

Though far from exhaustive, the following table is designed to help you consider both how pitfalls may present themselves and the consequences that may be felt from them:

	Initiation	Planning	Execution	Closing
Blame-storming (page 180)			Mistakes from previous phases or in the execution itself could be a temptation for blamestorming	Missed deadlines or unhappy stakeholders could trigger blamestorming behavior
Blowhard Jamboree (page 180)	Can manifest when defining the root causes of problems to be solved	Could occur during discussions or disagreements in the planning phase		
Group Think (page 181)	Could hamper ability to explore problems and find root causes	Could result in less creative designs and solutions	Verification or testing efforts may fail to consider diverse scenarios	

	Initiation	Planning	Execution	Closing
Heroics (page 181)		Heroics from the last project may affect expectations for the next, resulting in poor estimating, etc.	This is primarily where heroics occur	Looming delivery deadlines fuel heroics. "Heroes" may choose to leave the team rather than risk encountering a similar situation in the future
Intellectual Violence (page 182)	Can manifest when team is learning about the problem domain	Team members may be afraid to suggest creative solutions for fear of intellectual violence	A culture that allows intellectual violence may also encourage over-cautious work behaviors, slowing down the project	
Loose Cannon (page 182)	Can agitate stakeholders during initial requirements/specification gathering efforts	Difficult tasks such as estimating and planning become even more so with a loose cannon on the team	Team may be reluctant to remove loose cannon for fear of falling behind schedule	Individuals may be tempted to leave the team to avoid future projects with the loose cannon
Poor Project Team/ Stakeholder Relations (page 183)	Poor relations can result in inability to accurately define the problem and requirements/specifications	Poor relations or distrust may delay approval of the solution design, which is needed to move forward	Distrust may leave stakeholders assuming no progress is being made during long work periods	Acceptance or approval of the final work product may prove contentious, requiring multiple revisions as a result of the relationship breakdown
Wishful Thinking (page 183)	Team members may not properly grasp the importance of the problem statement, affecting everything from the solution itself to stakeholder analysis	Planning is ground zero for wishful thinking, with extremely optimistic schedules and ignored risks	Overly optimistic expectations may continue here, even when it's becoming quite obvious that things aren't going well	This is where the consequences of wishful thinking are most strongly felt. Teams should focus on lessons learned

	Initiation	Planning	Execution	Closing
Analysis Paralysis (page 184)	Analysis paralysis happens mostly during this phase	Paralysis may continue here, as the team is reluctant to get started		Late delivery and missed deadlines are the most common consequences of this early-project problem
Death March (page 184)		The conditions that cause a death march (unrealistic schedule, scope that is too large) typically occur during planning	As the project becomes more and more delinquent, morale drops	Team members who "stuck it out" must be rewarded appropriately after delivery or may leave
Fire Drill (page 185)	Delays in the beginning of the project are often the cause for fire drills		As deadlines approach and are consistently not met, the chaotic nature of a fire drill can worsen	
Ineffectively Adding Resources to the Team (page 186)	If contractors or external resources are to be used, they must be closely managed from the very beginning	As part of planning efforts, contingencies can be created that identify which resources may be most appropriate if needed	Looming deadlines can make adding resources tempting, but the wrong people can make the situation even worse	
Rushing to Execution (page 186)	Early phases are skipped or rushed to get to the "real work"	Requirements/ specifications efforts are skipped, designs are rushed and risks are not considered		Delayed delivery is the most common result of rushing to execution
Scope Creep (page 187)	Early on, an appropriate project scope is established	Some scope creep may occur during planning ("if we just did a bit more...")	Both the team and stakeholders can add to the scope in execution	The project triangle: increased scope requires more time or resources, resulting in a late or over-budget project

	Initiation	Planning	Execution	Closing
Silver Bullet (page 187)		A new tool, technology, or technique is proposed, and too little research or inflated expectations affect the project's schedule	Difficulties are encountered, and the "silver bullet" is revealed to be less productive than expected	Ultimately, the delivery date and/or budget is impacted

6.4   Summary and Conclusion

Although these pitfalls seem diverse, avoiding and resolving them long-term requires the following:

- An awareness of both what can happen and when it's most likely to occur,

- Diligence and continuous introspection,

- Management and leadership support, and

- A deliberate culture shift within the team and organization.

All of these criteria are necessary because projects and their teams continuously feel the *downstream* effects of events and decisions that have occurred beforehand. If a pitfall has previously occurred, changing the conditions that led to it requires a concerted effort by parties at all levels, or else it's likely to occur again.

As project leaders, we have the capacity to effect a change in all of these areas. One common excuse is to cite the powerlessness some project leaders feel within their larger organization—while it may not always be possible to affect the structures around you, it's important to realize that each project team can have its own "micro-culture." Within this micro-culture are possibilities that defy the larger norm— a project that effectively manages responsibility, priority, and communication, all while not losing sight of the goals and objectives that were set at initiation.

Nothing speaks louder than a successful leader and team completing a successful project. As a project leader, you have the power to leverage the *patterns* covered in this book—both the success you experience and the positive change you can enact within the world around you are limited only by your own perseverance and passion in applying the skills you've taken the time to gather and perfect. We hope this book has laid out the momentous challenge of leadership and the steps required to successfully make it happen.

Key Terms

Antipattern: A commonly-occurring behavior that usually proves to be counterproductive to those who engage in it. The antithesis of a *pattern* (page 179).

Downstream: The parts of a project or process that occur after a given point. For example, delivery is generally *downstream* to execution. Contrasts with *upstream* (page 188).

Pattern: A generally reusable solution to a common problem. The antithesis of an *antipattern* (page 179).

Thrashing: Non-productive, inefficient work effort caused by lack of organization and process (page 185).

Upstream: The parts of a project or process that occur before a given stage. For example, design is generally *upstream* to execution. Contrasts with *downstream* (page 188).

Review Questions

1. A team member starts a sentence with the words "most people think" but doesn't support their statement with any statistics. What may be occurring here?

2. Favoring visible progress, you supervisor has decided to move forward with some implementation before a key design has been completed. You know that this will result in more total work. Which pitfall is illustrated here?

3. Priorities seem to shift on a daily basis and you're worried that they will affect your team's productivity. What strategy could you implement to mitigate this reality?

4. You're worried that your team might be susceptible to the "heroics" pitfall. During which project phases is this most likely to occur?

5. Event "A" happened before event "B." What term describes event "A"'s relationship to event "B"?

Exercises

1. Your two-year shopping plaza architectural project has been in the planning phase for over a year and you believe analysis paralysis is a major factor. What are some scenario-specific strategies that may help here?

2. The team you manage has been assembled from several departments by your functional organization. One member has been a "loose cannon" lately, especially in how they've dealt with customers. Given that your resource may be hard to replace, how would you deal with this?

3. Pressure from management coupled with the team's eagerness to get started has rushed your e-commerce website project into the execution phase. What downstream implications could this have during the project? After its release?

4. In your organization, scope creep seems to be the norm. What actions can you take to prevent further expanding scope within your project? What are some strategies you can take to effect change in the larger organization?

Notes

[1]McConnell, Steve. *Rapid Development: Taming Wild Software Schedules*. Redmond, WA: Microsoft Press. p. 29. 1996.

[2]Koenig, Andrew. *Patterns and Antipatterns*. Journal of Object-Oriented Programming. 8 (1): 46–48. March–April 1995.

[3]Brown, William J., Malveau, Raphael C., McCormick, Hays W., Mowbray, Thomas J. Anti-Patterns - Refactoring software, architectures, and projects in crisis. John Wiley & Sons. p. 214. 1998.

[4]Whyte, W. H., Jr. "Groupthink". Fortune. p. 114–117, 142, 146. March 1952.

[5]Brown, William J., Malveau, Raphael C., McCormick, Hays W., Mowbray, Thomas J. Anti-Patterns - Refactoring software, architectures, and projects in crisis. John Wiley & Sons. p. 243. 1998.

[6]Blanchard, Ken. *Leadership and the One Minute Manager*. p. 38. 1985.

[7]Brown, William J., Malveau, Raphael C., McCormick, Hays W., Mowbray, Thomas J. Anti-Patterns - Refactoring software, architectures, and projects in crisis. John Wiley & Sons. p. 215-219. 1998.

[8]Parkinson, C. Northcote. *Parkinson's Law, or the Pursuit of Progress*. Penguin Books. 1958.

[9]Yourdon, Edward. *Death March: The Complete Software Developer's Guide to Surviving 'Mission Impossible' Projects*. Prentice Hall. 1999.

[10]McConnell, Steve. *Rapid Development: Taming Wild Software Schedules*. Redmond, WA: Microsoft Press. p. 47. 1996.

[11]Brown, William J., Malveau, Raphael C., McCormick, Hays W., Mowbray, Thomas J. Anti-Patterns - Refactoring software, architectures, and projects in crisis. John Wiley & Sons. p. 262-264. 1998.

[12]Brooks, Frederick P., Jr. *The Mythical Man-Month*. Addison-Wesley. 1975.

[13]Latane, B., Williams, K., and Harkins, S. *Many Hands Make Light the Work: The Causes and Consequences of Social Loafing*. Journal of Personality and Social Psychology, 37(6), p. 822-832. 1979.

[14]Brooks, Frederick P., Jr. *No Silver Bullet—Essence and Accident in Software Engineering*. Proceedings of the IFIP Tenth World Computing Conference. p. 1069–1076. 1986.

Appendix
Agile: The Future of Projects?

This appendix explores some new ideas in project management, concentrating mostly on Agile methods, values, and techniques, and how they can benefit a modern project team.

To many, Agile methods represent the cutting edge of how projects are carried out. Though many use it, and even more have heard of it, the word *Agile* itself is something of a "buzzword." Like many other buzzwords, some feel that they have a true understanding of what it means, dismissing others as uninformed, trend-following novices. Generally when the word *Agile* is used, it indicates one or more of the following ideas:

1. A group of process methods

2. A set of practices and tools

3. A defined set of core values and principles

Each of these three ideas is covered later in greater detail, but first it's important to understand where Agile originated and why it may be important to you.

A.1   The History of Agile

Agile ideas are rooted in the field of software engineering, a discipline that has allowed them to thrive.

Software engineering itself traces its linage to other engineering disciplines, especially computer engineering and electrical engineering. This history is important because these other fields were initially the place where software engineers sought insight on how to carry out projects. The established engineering process has always been the same: analyze the problem, design a solution, implement, verify it, and release. Moving slowly and carefully made a fair amount of sense for most projects: materials were expensive and the way a product was designed significantly impacted peoples lives—faulty products had the very real possibility of injuring customers and the reputations of the organizations producing them.

Software engineers, especially those working in project teams, found that working through each of these steps chronologically and thoroughly often resulted in well-engineered, successful software solutions. Larger projects took years to complete, but this was OK since at the time computers were quite expensive and the companies that needed large software solutions were accustomed to this type of process.

And then it wasn't OK. Software began to age, and companies began to realize that keeping it relevant to their current business models was costly, and, in many cases, a losing battle. Hardware prices dropped, and now small businesses and even private individuals could afford a computer, increasing demand for new products. The increasing availability of the internet brought new, instantaneous ways of distributing software as well as information sources to the masses. Software products were having trouble keeping up with the problems they were designed to solve, sometimes becoming obsolete before they were even released. All of this contributed to a growing dissatisfaction with traditional methods.

Evantually, a few innovators and thinkers began to address the problems that most directly affected them at their institutions and organizations—they dreamed of a lighter, more responsive way of working that took advantage of new business paradigms instead of resisting them. If a customer changes their mind, why not pivot with them? Why not take advantage of the fact that software has no material costs and can be changed quite easily? Why not deliver the software in smaller increments, instead of all at once at the end? Why not let teams organize themselves and choose how they will work together? Some chose to formalize these new ways of working, publishing them and working to build off of each other's ideas. In 2001, seventeen software engineers met and authored "The Manifesto for Agile Software Development,"[1] which directly included many of these ideas.

The idea of Agile has continued to adapt and change since 2001. For software engineers, it's no longer a new idea, but an everyday reality. Other fields have begun to take notice, and Agile has begun to make inroads in the way they carry out their projects. An example of its transition to the mainstream is evident at the core of project management itself: the latest edition of the Project Management Institute's *Guide to the Project Management Body of Knowledge* includes an *Agile Practice Guide* shrink-wrapped to it![2]

A.2   Why Agile is Important

Since their inception, the practitioners of any profession have been associated with the environment and set of tools with which they work. If you envision a team of architects, images of drafting tables and rolls of paper come to mind; chemical engineers work amongst test tubes and lab coats; civil engineers are surrounded by models of bridges and miniature city parks. But the modern reality of these jobs is starkly different—all of them, and many other project-related jobs consist of individuals working in front of computers. Whether designing a building, testing chemical interactions, or modeling city infrastructure, it all happens on a screen and is then saved as a file.

Though one may be tempted to lament the passing of older ways of working, the reality is that newer methods have been implemented because they're more efficient: they are easier, more cost effective, and more portable than their predecessors. Benefits have gone beyond cost savings though; today almost any job can be done from anywhere if circumstances—or preferences—warrant it. Architects can send their ideas to a colleague in an instant; chemical engineers no longer risk exposure to volatile substances; civil engineers can collaborate more readily with community stakeholders. Possibly the most important aspect of this evolution is that individuals on teams can work in concert with each other more effectively.

As described in the last section, Agile began with the software engineering community because the virtual, non-physical, relatively new work they were doing allowed for more flexibility. This granted them the freedom to experiment with new methods and ways of organizing work. This freedom is now available to other fields, and many leading organizations are leveraging Agile to their advantage. Because each field is different, the way in which they implement Agile will vary, but just as software engineers began by borrowing methods and practices from other, more established fields, other fields are now borrowing Agile from software engineering itself.

What is there to borrow? As previously mentioned, Agile can generally mean any of the following three ideas: a group of process methods, a set of practices and tools, or a defined set of core values and principles.[3]

A.3   Agile: A Group of Defined Processes

First and foremost, Agile refers to a set of processes (or methods) which emerged in response to the conditions discussed in the last section. Many define this as the *pure* or *true* meaning of "Agile," as it is the most all-encompassing application of the word. Agile processes are change-focused (discussed in chapter 2 on page 40), meaning that they are built to quickly respond to changing expectations and require continuous, intentional engagement with key stakeholders.

A large contrast is seen when comparing an Agile process with a more traditional plan-focused approach (page 37), especially when it comes to how often the project is expected to deliver visible results and the amount of documentation that is generated. Possibly the biggest contrast between them lies in their view of project scheduling. Plan-focused projects lean on sturdy, reliable timeframes, attempting to generate accurate models of how a project will progress over time.[4] Agile, change-focused projects rely on the combination of incrementally-delivered results and the wisdom of the team and key stakeholders to determine how things are progressing.

One common factor in all Agile methods is the effort to minimize the process as much as practically possible—because of this, it's important to follow all components of a given method as closely as possible, or risk leaving out a vital component. Generally, Agile methods work best for small teams of 3-9 people, optimizing lines of accountability and communication (see *The Complexity of Multiple Channels* on page 150)—Agile methods often don't scale gracefully beyond these small teams, though some methods of scaling them do exist.[5]

Though others exist, by far the most commonly used Agile method is called Scrum.[6] The most important feature of Scrum is its cyclical (iterative) nature. Each section of the process repeats in regular intervals. These sections, shown in the following diagram, are listed in the pages that follow. Note that Scrum's cyclical nature makes listing each one without referencing the others impossible.

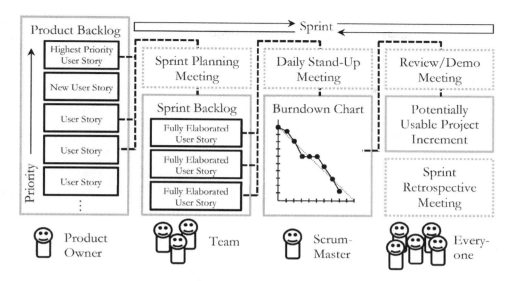

The Product Backlog

This is where the future of the project lives. The *Product Owner*, typically the customer, project sponsor, or major stakeholder "owns" this list. At any time, they are encouraged to add to, delete from, change, or reprioritize the *user stories* in this backlog. User stories are in many ways akin to requirements or specifications.

User Stories

User stories represent a single unit of work in a Scrum project. Tracking them through the process is the most visible evidence of work being completed. They are most often represented as a card, with a simple description of a stakeholder's desired outcome on the front and further details on the back. These "cards" may be physical or virtual:

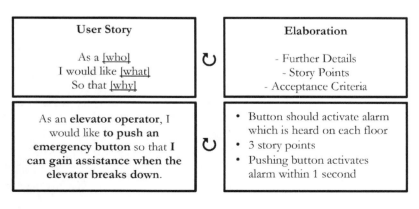

The Product Owner is often responsible for adding the user story itself: As a _____, I would like _____ so that _____. Writing the need, who needs it, and why it's needed represents the beginning of a conversation between the Product Owner and the team.

The results of this conversation are represented by the details on the back of the user story, known as *elaboration*. Elaboration may be added by anyone (most commonly the project team), and can include:

• Further details and clarifications needed to complete the user story.
• The *acceptance criteria*, specifying the conditions that are needed to declare the user story complete. Many would call this the user story's "test" or "verification".
• An estimate, typically a *story point* value, which establishes its difficulty in comparison to other stories.

Story Points and Planning Poker
When estimating effort for a user story, software engineering teams commonly use *story points* via an estimation process called "Planning Poker."[7] Using individual cards, each team member places their estimate in a pile face down. All estimates are revealed simultaneously and, if agreement is reached, the team moves on to the next estimate. Otherwise, the team discusses the factors that influenced their estimates and re-estimates until a consensus is reached. If consensus seems unlikely to happen, it's often because the user story needs more elaboration or needs to be broken up into two or more individual user stories.

When describing the important features of a user story, many refer to the acronym "INVEST":[8]

• **I**ndependent: User stories should have as little overlap as practical.
• **N**egotiable: User stories are not concrete, discussions may be needed.
• **V**aluable: Each story should be valuable to the Product Owner and support the objectives of the project.
• **E**stimate-able: If they are too unwieldy to understand, how can we know how long they will take?
• **S**mall: They should fit within one iteration, in this case a *sprint*.
• **T**estable: It should be obvious when the user story is or isn't done.

User stories "live" in a backlog, starting with the *product backlog* and migrating to the *sprint backlog*.

The Sprint Backlog

The sprint backlog is where user stories that are currently assigned to the project team live as the work they represent is being completed. In order to be moved from the product backlog to the sprint backlog, they must be fully fleshed-out and the team must clearly understand both how to complete the work and what conditions must be met to call it "done." The team "owns" the sprint backlog, which means they agree which stories are placed in it each *sprint* during the *sprint planning meeting*.

Sprints

A sprint is a single iteration of Scrum—the sprint cycle is the overarching cycle that a Scrum team follows. Sprints can vary in length, but many teams choose to make them two weeks. Within a sprint, each major element of Scrum is visited:

- An appropriate number of *user stories* are moved from the *product backlog* to the *sprint backlog*. This happens in the *sprint planning meeting*.
- The team works to complete each *user story* in the *sprint backlog*. Each day, the team holds a *daily stand-up meeting*.
- Completed *user stories* are tracked in the *burndown chart*.
- After the work cycle is completed, the *sprint review/demo meeting* is held.

The Daily Burndown Chart

When user stories are completed, their story point values are recorded on the daily burndown chart by the *Scrum Master*. The daily burndown chart is a basic line graph that plots the number of story points completed over time. This report shares a number of features with Variance and Earned Value Reports (covered in chapter 5 on page 169).

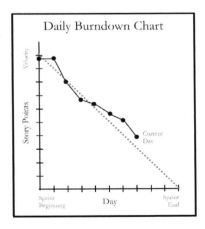

Scrum teams are encouraged to place this chart in a central area so that the progress being made by the team is apparent to everyone. Many include a "trend line" which indicates exactly how many story points are needed per day to keep on pace with the team's "Velocity" metric, or the number of story points they can typically complete in a sprint. Usually a burndown chart indicates progress for a single sprint, but there are variants that plot progress for greater increments.

Scrum Meetings

Because Agile processes depend so heavily on individual knowledge and effort rather than documentation and heavy process, there are several structured meetings that Scrum teams participate in:

- **Sprint Planning Meeting:** Before the sprint begins, it's important for the team to decide which user stories they plan to complete. This meeting, attended by both the team and the Product Owner, is designed to allow time to elaborate user stories, facilitate discussions about user story priority, and set goals for the next sprint. Because it's a "working meeting," it runs the danger of going quite long—teams should limit the length to about 2 hours per week of sprint length (so a two-week sprint should be no longer than 4 hours total).

- **Daily Stand-Up Meeting:** In this meeting (sometimes called a "Daily Scrum"), which is facilitated by the *Scrum Master*, team members answer three questions:
    - What did I do yesterday?
    - What am I planning to do today?
    - What is blocking my progress?

    This meeting is discussed in more detail in the next section (see page 205).

- **Sprint Review/Demo Meeting:** This occurs at the end of each sprint, and all team members and stakeholders are typically encouraged to attend. Attendees discuss what was accomplished during the sprint and are encouraged to demonstrate their work if possible. This meeting is usually informal, though there are time limits on both the length of the meeting itself (about an hour per sprint-week) and how long team members can spend preparing for it (one hour).

- **Sprint Retrospective Meeting:** In this meeting, the team looks back at what they've accomplished, answering three questions:
    - What should we *keep* doing?
    - What should we *stop* doing?
    - What should we *start* doing?

The team should ensure that is hasn't fallen prey to any of the common pitfalls listed in chapter 6, such as wishful thinking, heroics, or blamestorming. Additionally, discussing what is working well and the changes that should be made allow team members the opportunity to make improvements organically (which will, in turn, be discussed in future Sprint Retrospective Meetings).

Scrum Roles

Scrum only explicitly defines three roles, each of which are responsible for a part of the process:

- **The Product Owner:** The easiest way to think of the Product Owner is as the customer. They are responsible for communicating what the project needs to accomplish with the team. This happens in two ways:
  - **Managing user stories:** This means creating, prioritizing, and answering questions about them. Essentially, the Product Owner "owns" the product backlog.
  - **Providing input:** The Product Owner is expected to be highly available, but it's especially imperative that they're present for the sprint planning and review/demo meetings. (Working closely with the customer is one of Agile's core values, discussed in more detail starting on page 212.)

- **The Scrum Master:** This role consists primarily of facilitating the processes of Scrum; the Scrum Master is not the same as a formal project manager, and within some teams, the role rotates every few sprints. The Scrum Master "owns" the processes of Scrum, especially meetings such as the daily stand-up and artifacts such as the daily burndown chart.

- **The Team:** On a Scrum team, respect and accountability are extremely important. Scrum team members are skilled multidisciplinary professionals and represent the backbone of any successful project. Team members participate in the entire process, including managing backlogs, meetings, and delivering the project's results for the Product Owner's approval. Scrum teams most often follow the *interdisciplinary team structure*, which is covered in chapter 4 (see page 115).

"Is That All?"

Is this all there is to Scrum? The short answer is Yes. Agile methods are, by definition, simple. The longer answer is more complicated: because it is so popular, Scrum is also frequently modified, added to, and written about. Our world gains information from the internet, and software engineers have been talking about Agile and Scrum for over twenty years, primarily on the platforms they created themselves: blogs, social media, and online multimedia. Search the internet for the latest Agile trends and how they're being applied to projects worldwide.

A.4   Agile: A Set of Practices and Tools

After exploring Agile as a defined process (Scrum), you've probably noticed that there are a number of "components" that could be useful to your workflow even if implemented individually. This brings us to the second meaning of the word Agile: a set of practices and tools. As you read through them below, remember that Agile methods (and Agile practices) aren't a departure from "classic" project management, but rather variations in how a project is executed—the importance of leadership, communication, and prioritization are not diminished in any way.

The following could be considered the *best practices* of Agile:

Collective Ownership of Results

Collective ownership means that everyone on the team takes responsibility for the success of the entire project. To many this practice is among the most difficult—when an individual works hard to complete a portion of a project, it's easy for them and other team members to associate "ownership" of that portion to one individual. This can result in a hesitation by others to "mess with," add to, modify, or remove (even if needed) that portion of the project.

Successfully sharing ownership requires the team to meet each of the core needs listed in chapter 4: trust, managed conflict, commitment, accountability, and a results focus (see page 124). Maintaining shared ownership as the project progresses requires continuous attention by the project leader—all team members need to be aware of their commitment to collective ownership and need to monitor for the conditions mentioned above.

Continuous Integration and Version Control

Though most directly applicable to the development of software, the principles of continuous integration and version control can be applied to most modern workflows.

Continuous integration means integrating the work of individuals into the larger effort as frequently as practical. A team that is creating a user manual, for example, would add their individual parts to the master document several times a day. Working in this manner is designed to minimize the duplicated effort and rework associated with poor communication or misaligned distribution of tasks.

Version control is a concept designed to help increase work efficiency and make continuous integration of teams possible. Often facilitated by a server-based system, team members "check out" or "fork" portions of the work effort, complete it, and re-integrate it into the larger whole. It's quite easy to see how this could be useful to the user-manual team referenced above. In fact, most modern systems go even further, keeping every previous version, recording who changed what when, and even allowing multiple people to edit the same portion of a document simultaneously.

Daily Stand-Up Meetings

The practice of getting together for a few minutes at the beginning of the workday is not a new idea. Agile teems seek to maximize the benefits of checking-in while removing many of the problems of the traditional status meeting (see *It's a subject not appropriate for a meeting* on page 160):

- The team's identity is reinforced by coming together daily. Important issues such as planned absences are less likely to go unannounced.

- The preparation for and the meeting itself is *time-boxed* (time-boxing is discussed later in this section) as is the length of the meeting itself. Many teams require participants to physically stand (when practical) to encourage brevity.

- Peer-accountability is an important element of the daily standup meeting—most teams have each team member answer three questions:

  - What did I do yesterday?
  - What am I planning to do today?
  - What is blocking my progress?

Team members are aware of what their peers are or aren't accomplishing and whether they're directly impeding the progress of a teammate. Accountability is covered more thoroughly in chapter 4 (page 135).

- Many teams welcome anyone who wants to watch the meeting (increasing project visibility) while restricting their participation (i.e. talking) to keep it brief. If further discussion is needed, a conversation is planned after the conclusion of the standup meeting, allowing those not involved to get to work.

The meeting facilitator may vary; the project leader is often the best choice to hold the meeting, but organizational structure or specific processes may call for another facilitator (as discussed in the previous section, Scrum's daily standups are facilitated by the Scrum Master role).

Frequent Incremental Delivery

This concept entails the team striving to give stakeholders visible, meaningful progress early in the project, building on that project incrementally—a bit at a time. This principle lines up quite well with some of the process concepts outlined in chapter 2, namely cyclical (page 38) and change-focused (page 40) process models.

As discussed in the beginning of this appendix, many modern project teams work in a way similar to software teams: they create files and save them in a common space. Frequent incremental delivery often involves the relatively small step of taking what is being worked on and making it visible and understandable to appropriate stakeholders. Modern design principles, for example, may make it possible to build a virtual prototype rather than a physical model, making it much less expensive to show customers intermediate steps and gaining valuable feedback along the way.

When creating a product, frequent incremental delivery is much more straightforward: components are built to function and be added to incrementally—software is especially adept at following this principle, but other types of projects can reap its benefits as well.

Hybrid Project/Operations Teams

Project and operational teams (for more on operational work, see page 26) often find themselves at odds with one another. In many cases, project teams are responsible for developing new ideas, products, or services, and operational teams are responsible for the day-to-day operation and maintenance of them. When things don't go as planned, each group is tempted to blame the other—operations believes the original project had a flaw, and the project team insists that operations isn't implementing it correctly. Essentially, the culture (see page 10) of each team evolves separately, and complaining about the other team often becomes a significant part of that culture.

Creating teams which include members from both areas is an effective solution (software engineers call this "DevOps"—development and operations together). Because teams include members concerned with both the project and its eventual operation, and because they also work together daily, it becomes increasingly more difficult to blame each other for issues, identifying solely with one "side" or the other. Rather than feeling aligned with only the portion of the life cycle (page 29) they contribute to, teams instead are encouraged to share an identity related to the product, service, or solution they provide together.

In order to properly implement this type of team, several factors must be considered:

- **Will leadership and the basic organizational structure allow it?** Functional organizations (see page 31) may have an especially difficult time accommodating this type of team.

- **Products or services must be planned further out:** This requires thoughtful consideration to how work flows from its initial project to its long-term operational existence and beyond.

- **Can processes be modified to make the transition easier?** Additional workflow automation or increased documentation can be especially helpful to both the project team and operations. Ideally, they should work together to implement mutually-beneficial processes.

Many of the practices and tools included in this section have a strong potential to give this type of team the tools needed to be successful.

Kanban Boards

Kanban boards are used to visualize work in progress as well as how work flows throughout a project.[9] A simple illustration is shown below:

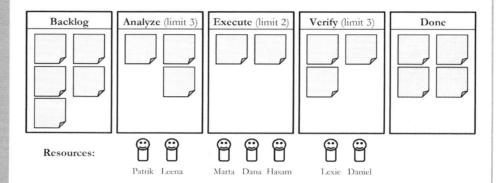

Each work unit is represented by a card, which flows through a series of steps. The main goal of Kanban is to eliminate wastefulness, which, for many projects, represents work waiting in queues or personnel waiting for others to complete their work. Kanban boards are designed to illustrate these bottlenecks and serve as a visual indicator of progress to the team and stakeholders. In an effort to alleviate inefficiencies, a team leader implementing Kanban can make adjustments in two areas:

1. **Personnel and resources can be moved to areas of more need:** Successfully using Kanban often requires an interdisciplinary team (see *Interdisciplinary Teams* on page 115), with members who are adept at filling more than one role.

2. **Work-in-progress limits can be placed on individual steps:** This can help minimize buildups that can lead to everything from waste to the lower morale associated with the inability to catch up (see *Fire Drill* on page 185).

Kanban boards can range in complexity from a simple piece of posterboard to the entire wall of an office—in either case, visibility and the elimination of inefficiencies should be the focus.

Team-Based Decision Making

As discussed in chapter 1, leadership can take on many different forms, but one of the most universally-recognized hallmarks of leadership is the authority to make decisions. The Agile concept of team-based decision making means that those in charge recognize the knowledge and abilities of the team and allows them to make important project decisions, stepping in only when needed. Benefits include:

- **A broader spectrum of knowledge:** Like risk identification and analysis (page 97), more team members means more diverse experiences, thought patterns, and elements of creativity—these are considered appropriately before reaching a conclusion.

- **Buy-in:** When team members are involved in the decision-making process and feel, at the very minimum, that they had input, they are more likely to approach the resulting work with enthusiasm and commitment.

- **Discouragement of absenteeism:** Not being present means not having a say in the decisions that are made. The scope of participation is widened, and when team members are absent during the decision-making process, their peers notice.

- **Identification as a team:** Even if some team members typically work as part of segmented sub-teams or as individuals, they need to come together to make decisions. This can help with cohesion and present opportunities for colleagues to better get to know each other.

Making team-based decisions requires team members who are ready, willing, and able to participate in the process. This means that each team member must value professionalism, ethics, and a team-focus over their own preferences or agenda. In some cases, team members may disagree—it's important that when consensus is reached and a decision is made that all team members are professional enough to wholeheartedly support the decision. If this doesn't seem possible, a more direct leadership model may be necessary (*Authoritarian / Commanding / Autocratic*, for example, covered on page 3).

As difficult as it may seem for team members, team-based decision making can mean even more responsibility for team leaders or management. Facilitating the process of reaching a decision can be difficult

at times, especially if schedules don't line up or there are issues with individual team members' personalities (disagreeability or non-committal behavior). Ceding control can be difficult for some during the decision-making process, but when things don't go well after the fact it can be excruciating—like team members, leaders must resist the urge to seek blame (see *Blamestorming* on page 180), working instead to develop and implement solutions.

Time-Boxing

Though most types of work seem to have their own "rhythm," the practice of time-boxing establishes defined, specific periods of time in which the team completes specified tasks. One example is the *sprint* (covered in the last section on page 201), where the team works incrementally within predefined "time-boxes." A smaller, more practical example could include limiting meeting times or meeting preparation times.

Though it requires a fair amount of discipline to implement, time-boxing has the potential to offer some advantages to teams and projects:

- If the work cycle is time-boxed, the smaller increments of work can improve tracking visibility.

- If the project runs the risk of becoming reactive (see *Fire Drill* on page 185), time-boxing can promote short-term stability while allowing for relatively quick reaction time—often the next time-boxed increment.

- If the project's scope (covered on page 50) is difficult to define, teams can instead choose to set a time-box, working until the time limit is reached and deciding at that point what to do next.

- Teams may choose to time-box undesirable or repetitive work, so that they can properly share responsibility or limit negative effects. For example, military units may share "night-watch" guard duty, ensuring that each member of the team shoulders equal responsibility.

User Stories

User stories represent the stakeholder's view of the project's expected outcomes, which the team commitments to understanding before working on that part of the project. User stories are covered more extensively in the previous section starting on page 199.

Working in Pairs

This involves two individuals working together, with one completing the tasks and the other watching. As discussed at the beginning of this chapter, modern teams are very likely to be completing their work on a computer. Working as a pair means sharing only one computer. The second person focuses entirely on what the first is doing, offering suggestions or guidance as

needed—they are not using a second computer or conducting research. At regular intervals the two team members switch places, the watcher now the worker and vice-versa.

Completing work as a pair offers some essential advantages:

- Because "two heads are better than one," work-stopping issues are less likely to occur.

- People are more likely to stay on task.

- It promotes a culture of mentorship and cross-training.

- The chance of only a single person understanding part of the project is reduced, improving collective ownership of the project and knowledge sharing among team members.

- If work reviews or testing are a part of the project, this can catch or prevent issues earlier in the project cycle (upstream), making them less detrimental to the final outcome.

Though there are many advantages, a few disadvantages may appear:

- More interpersonal interaction is required, and this can be draining for some team members.

- Though studies have shown that the practice can increase quality significantly,[10] there may be a perception that less work is being done.

- Odd-sized teams, especially small ones, may "leave someone out."

The Agile practices listed above represent only a percentage of the practices used by Agile teams all over the world. You are encouraged to seek out others or to create your own. A solid understanding of the *values* and *principles* of Agile, covered in the next section, is vital in implementing any such practice.

A.5 Agile: A Defined Set of Core Values and Principles

Now that you've gained some insight into Agile's processes and practices, it's important to understand the values and principles behind them. In 2001, a group of industry leaders formalized a set of 4 guiding values and 12 supporting principles known as the Agile Manifesto.[1] This document doesn't represent the establishment of Agile as a philosophy; rather, it was designed to help those who chose to implement Agile to understand the attitudes and beliefs that spawned the processes, practices, and tools they are using.

Agile Values

The following values are designed to help organizations and teams implementing Agile understand the preferred "mentality," or overarching approach to their work:

- **Individuals and interactions over processes and tools:** Agile organizations choose to value the team and their interactions over the particular way teams choose to do work.

- **Working solutions over comprehensive documentation:** Agile teams place the solution they are creating as the highest priority, especially over the artifacts and process used to create it.

- **Customer collaboration over contract negotiation:** Agile prioritizes time spent understanding customer needs over the certainty of ironclad agreements (schedules, precise specifications, etc.).

- **Responding to change over following a plan:** Agile promotes the understanding that modern business values agility (the ability to adapt to changes) over the fear of broken plans.

Supporting Principles

In addition to the 4 values, there are 12 principles designed to clarify how Agile teams work. They focus on different aspects of the project.

1. **The stakeholders:** For many organizations the biggest departure from the norm is that in Agile projects, the "customer" (not the team) sets priority.

   - The team must *welcome changing requirements/specifications*, even late in the process. Though changes are inconvenient, Agile's teams are happy to accommodate them as early as possible. The more "upstream" the better, but accommodating a change late in the project is better than having to deal with it after completion.

   - The highest priority is *stakeholder satisfaction*, with a preference for early and continuous delivery of value. Agile's iterative and incremental approach are key factors in demonstrating visible progress to stakeholders.

   - Close, *daily cooperation between business people and the team* is a must. This means that both the team and important stakeholders must consistently make themselves available for discussion, choosing to work in close vicinity. The communication principles covered in chapter 5 become even more important.

2. **The organization:** Agile projects also mean a commitment from the organization to entrust team members with the power and environment to succeed.

   - Projects are built around *motivated individuals, who should be trusted to get the job done*. Ideally, leadership is primarily concerned with removing barriers and providing a work-friendly environment, rather than directing each task to its completion.

- A co-located (all in one workspace) team is preferred, and *face-to-face conversation* is considered the best form of communication. Co-location is an important part of Agile largely because of its minimized documentation (a core value). Non-co-located team members can make discoveries or make decisions, and with minimized documentation and no one else there to share these with, the new information and work efficiencies are often simply lost.

- The best teams also are *self-organizing*. By allowing teams to determine the conditions that surround them as well as how they carry out their work, the organization is demonstrating both commitment to and trust in the individuals that make up their teams. This also implies that existing team members should have some input into the hiring process for new team members.

- In an environment that embraces change, working at a *sustainable pace* must be prioritized. When following a plan, teams may be tempted to perform heroics (a pitfall covered on page 181) near the end of the project. Agile teams may be tempted to do this as well, but it's important for the team to have the self discipline to maintain a constant pace regardless of the ever-changing circumstances of the project.

3. **The way work is done:** In addition to how customer interaction occurs and how the organization views the team, Agile projects take a distinct approach in their work practices.

- First and foremost, the team understands that a working product, feasible design, or demonstrated result is to be *delivered as frequently as possible* (weeks rather than months).

Is "Agile" Faster?

Many hear the term "Agile" and assume that the result is a shorter schedule. In this case, the term refers to the fact that these processes focus on their responsiveness to changes in customer or market need (see *Change-Focused Process Models* on page 40). In general, Agile projects are not completed any faster than their traditional, plan-focused counterparts; instead, they deliver incrementally, which means visible results appear earlier in the project cycle, but the volume of those results is often no different than those in efficient plan-focused projects (covered on page 37).

- The team should focus primarily on *project deliverables, not artifacts.* This work is considered the principle measure of the project's progress. Artifacts are merely the tools needed to create better deliverables.
- The team should pay *continuous attention to excellence and good design* as they work. Each individual takes personal responsibility for the quality of both their own work and the project at large, monitoring for and fixing issues to the best of their ability as quickly as possible. When iterative or incremental processes are used, the temptation always exists to put things off until later—this must be actively resisted.
- In their work, teams should also strive for *efficiency and simplicity* in both their process and the designed outcomes of the project. The Agile Manifesto defines this essential simplicity as "the art of maximizing the amount of work not done."
- Finally, the team must regularly *reflect on how to become more effective* and make appropriate adjustments to their interaction, process, and execution. This is often called a *retrospective.* Scrum teams hold a meeting each sprint to accomplish this (page 202).

After reading these values and principles, it becomes obvious how the Agile philosophy views project work: As a face-to-face endeavor carried out by competent and empowered individuals who deeply care about the success of their project. Does this describe your team and organization? The next section breaks down some of the essential elements needed for any organization to properly embrace Agile's way of doing things.

A.6   Implementation in Your Organization

Understanding Agile's methods, tools, and values is essential to implementing it in any organization, but there is also a set of conditions that must be present to implement Agile successfully. The majority of these conditions are so essential to Agile that if they are not present, it's unlikely the organization would benefit at all. They are as follows:

- **External factors allow it:** Examples of conditions that may make Agile impractical include tight security procedures, a requirement for heavy documentation, or industry/government regulations that standardize procedure.

- **The appropriate type of customer:** Though the projects may not have an external, formal "customer," someone needs to be engaged with the team, to fulfill the role of Scrum's Product Owner, for example.

"What About Contracts?"

Traditional project contracts try to "nail down" all three sides of the project triangle—the scope of the project, its schedule, and the resources available along the way (see page 46). Agile's commitment to "embracing change" makes this all but impossible. Completing projects with an Agile mentality requires a different kind of business relationship—one of frequent, face-to-face communication between people who trust each other. Contracts for Agile projects often define either the time to work together or the scope of what's to be done, but not both—doing this wouldn't be "Agile."

- **Reasonably small projects:** When a project has a massive team, multi-year schedule, or a lot of moving parts, Agile's lower level of upfront planning can be a detriment. Smaller projects benefit the most from Agile processes and practices.

- **Strong, experienced team members:** Agile minimizes process and relies heavily on experienced, self-motivated team members—failure to meet both of these conditions can spell disaster for someone who is just beginning to learn the trade.

Team Member Motivation

Agile requires strong, experienced team members—but how are they motivated? Many of the basic motivators covered in chapter 1 (page 7) relate directly to Agile's way of approaching project work. Recognition for hard work is inherent in the Daily Standup (page 205); interpersonal relationships are a central theme of Agile's values and principles, and intrinsically-motivated team members often find the team autonomy and the management's trust in their abilities quite motivating.

- **Executive support:** Like any organizational decision, leadership needs to not only give permission, but actively promote and support it. Agile processes and practices represent a fundamental cultural change, and managers at all levels must be on board.

Transitioning to Agile

The reasons for embracing a more Agile way of executing projects are now clear; your team (and customer) seems to meet all of the conditions above, and you're excited to move forward. What is the next step?

Though you may be tempted to "jump in feet first" and commit your organization to a new, more Agile lifestyle, maximizing the chance of success requires a deliberate, measured approach. Many organizations choose to run a "pilot" program, in which only a few project teams make the transition at a time. Once their change proves beneficial, executives and other teams are more likely to be comfortable with implementing the change in their area of influence. A "cold turkey" approach, in which the entire organization transitions simultaneously, is quite risky, though in some situations it has been successful.

If you are on a team that is making this type of change, it's important to follow a few basic guidelines:

- **The change must be "organic":** Both the need for a change and the change itself must occur naturally. Rushing or forcing a transition can disrupt work being done and may cause team members to form negative, misrepresented opinions of Agile processes, tools, and values.

- **The team must frequently reflect on their progress:** One of the 12 principles listed in the last section, retrospection, is even more essential at the beginning of a transition. Retrospectives can reveal difficulties, resistance, and inefficiencies caused by the change to Agile.

- **You must be willing to be uncomfortable:** Heavier process and documentation help many teams feel comfortable with the unique project they are engaging in. Agile, which is adaptive by nature, fails when teams become too "predictive," trying to plot everything out ahead of time.

- **Start with well-defined Agile processes and practices:** As much as possible, the team should follow a defined Agile process such as Scrum (covered earlier in this chapter on page 198) and "pure" Agile practices or tools. This means resisting the urge to change or add things too early—most often these additions will be previously used, "non-Agile" practices. Doing this before the team has a solid, foundational understanding of the process or practice will often undermine its effectiveness—and simplicity (an Agile principle).

- **Project functions must still be performed:** An exciting new way of doing things may make it easy to neglect important ongoing project activities such as communication (chapter 5) and risk management (page 97). The fundamental benefits of these important functions are still essential to project success. Agile teams may choose to redistribute how the work is done, but they should by no means neglect it. Project functions are discussed on page 28.

- **Don't expect reduced project completion times:** Being "Agile" may lead some to believe that projects will be done faster and cheaper. Remember that Agile's benefits lie in its ability to respond to change and intuitions of the customer and team. Organizations implementing Agile hope that the project's end result is more in line with what their stakeholders need—if they are hoping for quicker, cheaper outcomes, they are likely to be disappointed (especially in the short term).

More than anything, movement towards Agile involves an intentional shift in priorities.

- Rather than resisting change (especially later in the project), can we move towards accepting and ultimately embracing it?
- Can we trust our team members, not just managers, to know what's best?
- Do we want to work face-to-face with stakeholders daily?
- Can we commit to highly visible, incrementally-delivered work?
- Do we have the discipline to resist older, more comfortable ways of doing things?
- Can we see ourselves honestly discussing our flaws and how to fix them?

If the answer to these questions is "yes," then you, your team, and your organization just might benefit from embracing a more Agile culture. How that change is to be executed is as unique as your team and organization.

A.7   Summary and Conclusion

Though project work completed in an Agile way may feel different, it's still prone to many circumstances that would make any project fail. Agile or otherwise, leadership needs to be appropriate for the team, communication is important, and support from stakeholders at all levels is vital.

Originally implemented by software engineers, Agile processes, practices, and values are proving more and more applicable to project teams in other industries. A more responsive, relevant project outcome becomes possible when organizations and teams commit to more direct interactions with stakeholders, simpler work-flows, and the belief in placing trust in the members of their team.

Implementing Agile can't be done blindly. It requires intentional planning and follow-through as individual teams and larger organizations purposely change their culture. Everyone must participate—executive management, project leadership, team members, and stakeholders. Agile organizations focus most of all on the people who make up the project team and stakeholders and becomes a real advantage if executed properly.

Key Terms

Backlog: A prioritized list of work to be done. The *Scrum* process includes a product backlog and *sprint* backlog, each containing *user stories* (page 199, 201).

Daily Stand-Up: A short daily meeting where each team member gives status, plans, and impediments. Designed to increase team accountability (page 205).

Retrospective: Honestly looking at what has and hasn't worked in order to make improvements going forward. Agile teams often meet specifically to look at their work retrospectively (page 202).

Scrum: An iterative and incremental process for managing and completing project work. Scrum is the most popular of several Agile processes methods (page 198).

Sprint: A set period of time in which a team works on a predefined set of objectives. *Scrum* teams work on items in the sprint *backlog* during the *time-boxed* sprint (page 201).

Time-Boxing: The act of allocating a fixed period of time, a "time-box" to an activity. For example, proper meeting agendas (including *daily stand-ups*) set these limits to prevent wasting time (page 210).

User Story: A short description of what the primary stakeholder wants (for the project) and why. Used by most Agile teams, it often uses the format "As a __, I would like __ so that __." User stories are then expanded to include all of the information needed to implement them (page 199).

Review Questions

1. From which field did Agile emerge?

2. In the Scrum process, who is responsible for adding, removing, or prioritizing user stories in the product backlog?

3. Well-written user stories follow the INVEST acronym. What does the "N" stand for?

4. Scrum's Daily Burndown Chart includes a "Velocity" metric. What does this metric indicate?

5. Team members participating in a Daily Stand-Up Meeting answer three important questions. What are they?

6. The Agile Manifesto lists 4 main values. Which one is most related to the word "Agile"?

7. According to the Agile Manifesto,   8. Are "Agile" projects generally com-
   what is considered the best form of   pleted faster?
   communication?

Exercises

1. Agile's foundation lies in software engineering's culture. Given what you've
   learned about Agile processes, practices, and values, what elements of *your* profession's culture (your work practices, etc.) seem incompatible with that of software engineering and Agile? Why?

2. You are implementing a project which seeks to update a community youth center
   recreational room. The room currently has two well-warn billiard tables, a pinball
   game, and several dozen board games. Write five basic user stories for this
   project. Be sure to include multiple stakeholder perspectives (youth, parents,
   employees, etc.) as well as reasoning for each.

3. A Scrum sprint planning meeting can take several hours to complete, leading
   participants to feel unenthusiastic about participating in such an endeavor. Using
   what you've learned about the meeting's purpose and the meeting guidelines
   covered in chapter 5 (page 159), create a 10-item checklist to be verified before
   the meeting begins.

4. Your team has been tasked with producing a new type of ice cream that includes
   a vanilla mixture with 3 ingredients, with each of the three requiring progressively
   more time to prepare and mix in. The ingredients (which all must remain frozen)
   are extremely temperature sensitive and must remain outside of the freezer for
   as little time as possible while preparing and mixing them in. Create a Kanban
   board that the team might use to minimize waste and maximize productivity.

5. After reading about Agile's practice of working in pairs, you've been considering
   reorganizing your team to work in this way the majority of the time. Excluding
   those listed in the text starting on page 211, list one potential advantage and one
   potential disadvantage of working in pairs.

6. Agile culture places high value on teams that meet with their stakeholders face-
   to-face on a daily basis. Your team feels that implementing Agile processes and
   practices is a great idea, but your customer is only able to be at your office
   once a month. What are some other communication options that would provide

similar benefits to a local customer (face-to-face communication and spontaneous availability)? What problems could they present?

7. Looking at the list of questions on page 218, which priorities are likely to be the most difficult for your industry or organization to embrace? Why? What existing priorities compete with those of Agile?

Notes

[1]Kent Beck, James Grenning, Robert C. Martin, Mike Beedle, Jim Highsmith, Steve Mellor, Arie van Bennekum, Andrew Hunt, Ken Schwaber, Alistair Cockburn, Ron Jeffries, Jeff Sutherland, Ward Cunningham, Jon Kern, Dave Thomas, Martin Fowler, and Brian Marick (2001). *Manifesto for Agile Software Development.* Agile Alliance. Retrieved November 2107.

[2]PMBOK Guide, 6th Edition released in 2017. ISBN 9781628253825. https://www.pmi.org/pmbok-guide-standards/foundational/pmbok/sixth-edition

[3]Many elements of this appendix are based on the work of Schwaber, Ken and Sutherland, Jeff. *The Scrum Guide—The Definitive Guide to Scrum: The Rules of the Game* (Creative Commons Share-Alike). http://www.scrumguides.org/docs/scrumguide/v2017/2017-Scrum-Guide-US.pdf. November 2017.

[4]This well-crafted sentence appeared in a paper authored by Ian Parfit in my Spring 2017 Agile class. Used with permission.

[5]Sutherland, Jeff. *Agile Can Scale: Inventing and Reinventing SCRUM in Five Companies.* Cutter IT Journal Vol. 14, No. 12. p. 5-11. 2001.

[6]*The 11th Annual State of Agile Report.* VersionOne. https://explore.versionone.com/state-of-agile/versionone-11th-annual-state-of-agile-report-2. Accessed December 2017.

[7]Grenning, James. *Planning Poker or How to avoid analysis paralysis while release planning.* Wingman Software. https://wingman-sw.com/papers/PlanningPoker-v1.1.pdf. 2002.

[8]Wake, Bill. *INVEST in Good Stories and SMART Tasks.* Exploring Extreme Programming. https://xp123.com/articles/invest-in-good-stories-and-smart-tasks/. 2003.

[9]Anderson, David J. *Kanban: Successful Evolutionary Change for Your Technology Business.* Blue Hole Press. 2010.

[10]Cockburn, Alistair and Williams, Laurie. *The Costs and Benefits of Pair Programming.* Proceedings of the First International Conference on Extreme Programming and Flexible Processes in Software Engineering (XP2000). 2000.

Answers to Review Questions

Chapter 1 (page 21)

1. Laissez-faire (page 4)
2. They're both team-focused, requiring team members to be able to converse with each other (page 3)
3. Expert and referent (page 6)
4. Mastery/exploration (page 8)
5. Extrinsic (page 8)
6. Stakeholders (page 12)
7. The concept of culture, among others (page 10)
8. Customers and management (page 12)
9. Protecting information and the project (page 15)

Chapter 2 (page 75)

1. Unique goals and outcomes (page 26)
2. Project sponsor (page 25)
3. Execution phase (page 27)
4. The chapter includes Risk Management, Quality Assurance, Communications Management, and Project Management, but there are other examples (page 28)
5. Functional (page 31)
6. Plan-focused (page 37)
7. The scope statement (page 53)
8. The executive summary (page 63)

Chapter 3 (page 108)

1. Comparison or analogy estimation (page 81)

2. Bottom-up estimation (page 81)
3. 1-2 resources 1-2 weeks per activity/task (page 83)
4. Precision (page 85)
5. Calculated as 620/1350 or 45.9% complete (page 95)
6. 1 week (page 99)
7. Keep satisfied (page 104)

Chapter 4 (page 146)

1. Interdisciplinary team (page 112, 115)
2. Problem-resolution team (page 113)
3. Top-down teams (page 114)
4. Treat them as a stakeholder (page 117, 12, 103)
5. Elicitation, organization, and reporting (page 120)
6. Norming (page 123)
7. Forcing (page 129)
8. The leader, the team, and the individual team members (page 130)
9. To one's peers (page 135)
10. "A"-accountable (page 137)

Chapter 5 (page 177)

1. 3 channels are added for a total of 6 $[(n(n-1))/2]$ (page 150)
2. Paralingual and verbal communication (page 153)
3. Interactive (page 154)
4. Cancel or reschedule the meeting (page 159)
5. Honesty or truthfulness (page 162)

6. Public metrics (page 164)
7. Variance (page 166)
8. Trend/forecasting report (page 168)

Chapter 6 (page 193)

1. Blowhard jamboree and/or weasel words (page 180)
2. Rushing to execution (page 186)
3. Fire drill pitfall, strategy: project management sheltering (page 185)
4. Execution and delivery (page 189)
5. Upstream (page 188)

Appendix (page 220)

1. Software Engineering (page 195)
2. The Product Owner (page 199)
3. Negotiable (page 200)
4. Number of story points completed per sprint (page 201)
5. What did I do yesterday? What am I planning to do today? What is blocking my progress? (page 205)
6. Responding to change over following a plan (page 213)
7. Face-to-face communication (page 214)
8. Generally not (page 214, 218)

Index

About the Author

Samuel A. Malachowsky is a certified career Project Manager (PMP) who currently teaches in the Software Engineering Department at the Rochester Institute of Technology. His passion lies in connecting the abstract and technical with the practical—by teaching project values, leadership, and personal professional development. His articles, along with more information about the ideas presented in this book, are available at TeachingSE.com. He currently resides in Rochester, NY with his wife and children.

Additionally, Samuel is available for consultation and on-site training for the areas covered in this book by emailing info@TeachingSE.com.

22513264R00135

Made in the USA
Columbia, SC
28 July 2018